MW00561795

PHYSICS FOR AVIATION

by
Sister Noel Dreska, Ph.D.
and
Leonard Weisenthal, Ph.D.

International Standard Book Number 0-89100-411-4
For sale by: IAP, Inc., A Hawks Industries Company
Mail To: P.O. Box 10000, Casper, WY 82602-1000
Ship To: 7383 6WN Road, Casper, WY 82604-1835
(800) 443-9250 ❖ (307) 266-3838 ❖ FAX: (307) 472-5106
HBC1092 Printed in the USA

Printed in the United States of America

Library of Congress Cataloging-in-Publication Data

Dreska, Noel, 1928–
     Physics for aviation / by Noel Dreska and Leonard Weisenthal.
        p.   cm.
     ISBN 0-89100-411-4 (pbk.) : $16.95
        1. Physics.   2. Aeronautics.   I. Weisenthal, Leonard, 1946–
II. Title.
   QC23.D79   1992
   530'.0246291--dc20
                                                    92-27173
                                                       CIP

Table of Contents

Introduction

The year 1901 saw Wilbur and Orville Wright rapidly gaining experience piloting the second of their gliders. In designing this glider, the Wrights had adhered to aeronautical information reported over the previous century by other flight enthusiasts. By the end of the year, however, frustrated by the mediocre performance of their craft, the brothers abandoned all second hand information and set out on their own investigation. They built a wind tunnel and a force balance with which they measured the lift and drag on over two hundred airfoil shapes. The result of these measurements was a third glider which had its maiden flight on the last day of summer in 1902. Over one thousand successful flights of this glider were made in the remainder of that year setting new distance and time records while producing two very capable pilots and placing the Wright brothers at the threshold of powered flight.

This short historical sketch illustrates one instance in which careful measurement aided in bringing about a profound advance in the field of aviation. The modern aviation industry utilizes measurement in all aspects of research, development, maintenance, and operation of aircraft.

The aviation mechanic is routinely called upon to make measurements in a variety of circumstances for the purpose of testing, maintaining, and repairing aircraft systems. For example, compression checks have to be made on aircraft engine cylinders, track check measurements are routinely performed on airplane propellers and helicopter rotor blades. Feeler gauges are used to measure turbine blade clearances. Manifold pressure gauges and altimeters are calibrated using barometers. The proper loading of aircraft requires weight and balance checks utilizing scales and length measurement.

Chapter I

Measurements and Units

Length Measurements

Let us measure the length of the bar shown in figure 1-1. Suppose that it is measured with the meter stick placed next to the bar. Note that the meter stick has a length that can be expressed as 100 centimeters.

We can judge that the length of the bar is 76 cm. We are sure of the digit 7 but have estimated that the second digit is a 6. We write the measurement as 76 cm. We have expressed the length of the bar with a measurement having two significant digits.

In figure 1-2, we can see that the second digit was a 5 and we can estimate a third digit to be an 8. Our measurement this time, using a different ruler, is expressed as 75.8 cm. Note that we now have three significant digits in our measurement.

In our first measurement (figure 1-1) we have written two significant digits and in the second (figure 1-2) we have used three significant digits. In one case we wrote 76 cm and in the other case we wrote 75.8 cm. Engineers are very careful in recording measurements. A measurement of 76 cm indicates that the measuring instrument that was used was capable of telling us that the 7 was a certain digit and the 6 was an estimated digit. That was the best that particular ruler could do! When the second ruler was used it was possible to record 7 and 5 as certain digits. The 8 was an estimated or uncertain digit.

Whenever a measurement is recorded the last recorded digit is always an estimated digit. The same procedure is used for the measurement of any quantity. The examples that follow should clarify the procedure.

Measured Quantities and Exact Quantities

There are two different kinds of quantities: measured quantities and exact quantities. Exact quantities are quantities that can be counted. For example, there are exactly 24 students in a given physics class. It is meaningless to speak of 24.23 students. Measured quantities are quantities that are obtained by a system of measurement such as that discussed above.

When a measured quantity is multiplied or divided by an exact quantity, the result is a quantity that has the same number of significant digits as the measured quantity. For example, if the measurement 23.4 cm is multiplied by the exact number 2, the product is 46.8 cm.

When two measured quantities are multiplied or divided by each other, the result obtained should be rounded off to the number of significant digits as in the least accurate of the two measured quantities.

For example, if the length of a rectangle is measured as 4.32 cm and the width of this rectangle

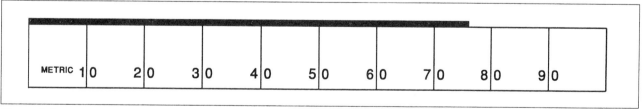

Figure 1-1.

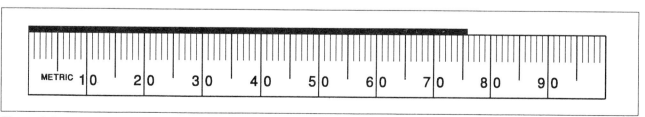

Figure 1-2.

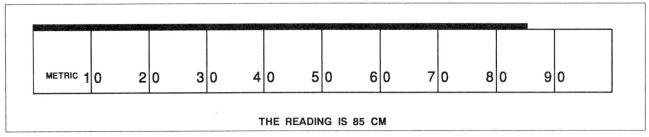

THE READING IS 85 CM

Figure 1-3.

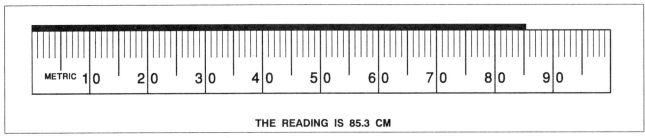

THE READING IS 85.3 CM

Figure 1-4.

is measured as 1.21 cm, the area can be calculated by multiplying the two dimensions.

4.32	The last digit is uncertain.
<u>1.21</u>	<u>The last digit is uncertain.</u>
432	This entire line is uncertain.
864	The last digit is uncertain.
<u>432</u>	<u>The last digit is uncertain.</u>
5.2272	The last three digits in this line are uncertain, since at least one of the added digits is uncertain.

It is meaningless to express the area with three uncertain digits. Instead, we write the area as 5.23 sq. cm or 5.23 cm^2. Note that writing the area in this way indicates that the 5 and 2 are certain digits and the 3 is an uncertain digit. Note also that we wrote the final uncertain digit as a 3 and not a 2. We did this because the fourth digit was 5 or more.

You may have noticed that in all of the above examples we have dealt with the digits 1, 2, 3, 4, 5, 6, 7, 8, or 9. We have not included the digit zero in any of our examples. The zero digit presents difficulties that the other nine digits do not present. The zero digit has two functions. Sometimes it is a significant digit and other times it is merely a "place holder". A place holder tells us the correct size of a number. It must be in a number to tell us the "order of magnitude" of this number. One important rule to remember is that a zero following

a decimal point is significant only if it also follows another significant digit. In the examples below, we will clarify the method of dealing with zeros in our calculations.

In our course, we will assume that all measurements given in any problem are measured with instruments that are capable of giving a result accurate to three significant digits. This means that in calculating results we will round off all answers to three significant digits.

In figure 1-5, we will calculate areas of rectangles by multiplying the measured length by the measured width.

Round-Off Error

Sometimes there is a difficulty when a series of calculations must be performed.

Suppose that, as in the type of calculation that will follow in the next section, a series of calculations must be performed. For example, it may be necessary to square one measured quantity and divide by another measured quantity.

$$\text{answer} = \frac{(\text{one measured number})^2}{\text{another measured number}}$$

When this type of calculation is done it is best to square the number in the numerator, and then, without clearing your calculator, divide by the number in the denominator. However, sometimes it is helpful to some students to write down the answer obtained by squaring the number in the numerator first, rounding off that result, and doing the problem in two steps. Both methods are acceptable. However, the answers obtained may differ slightly in the third significant digit. Since the third significant digit is always an uncertain digit anyway, we can understand why this difference occurs. An example will illustrate the difficulty.

EXAMPLE 1-A.

Suppose that we must calculate the result of squaring 15.5 and then dividing by 25.8.

$$\text{Method 1:} \qquad \frac{(15.5)^2}{25.8} = 9.31$$

Calculator not cleared until final result.

$$\text{Method 2:} \qquad \frac{(15.5)^2}{25.8} = \frac{240}{25.8} = 9.30$$

The rounded-off result of the operation of squaring was written in the middle step.

Both results would be considered correct. Note that the difference in the last significant digit is only one unit. Recall also that the zero in 9.30 and the one in 9.31 are both uncertain digits. Therefore we should not be disturbed about the fact that both results give a "correct" answer.

Finally, remember that there will be a difference of only one, or possibly two, digits in the last significant digit.

The Aspect Ratio of an Airplane Wing

Some simple calculations relating to airplane wings will now give us an opportunity to apply what we have discussed about significant digits. Figure 1-6 shows the projection of a wing. The distance (b) from wing tip to wing tip, is referred to as the span. The distance from the leading edge of the wing to the trailing edge is called the chord. Since the chord of most wings is not a constant, a mean or average chord (c) is defined.

Early in the history of aviation, it became evident that the ratio of the span to the average chord was an important parameter for determining the aerodynamics of a wing. This ratio is referred to as the aspect ratio (AR) and can be written.

$$AR = \frac{b}{c}$$

A Boeing 747 has a wing span of 59.64 meters and an average chord of 8.57 meters. Determine the aspect ratio.

$$AR = \frac{59.64 \text{ m}}{8.57 \text{ m}} = 6.96$$

The product of average chord and the span is the area of the wing (S). Note that the wing area can be expressed algebraically by the expression bc.

Therefore, we can form a new formula for the aspect ratio by multiplying numerator and denominator by b.

(LENGTH)	(WIDTH)	CALCULATOR READING	ANSWER ROUNDED OFF TO THREE SIGNIFICANT DIGITS
(4.35 cm)	(1.30 cm)	5.655	5.66 cm^2
(35.9 m)	(450 m)	16155	16200 m^2
(0.123 mm)	(0.217 mm)	0.026691	0.0267 mm^2
(3420 mi)	(1210 mi)	4138200	4140000 mi^2
(4.12 m)	(0.186 m)	0.76632	0.766 m^2
(34.8 ft.)	(12.7 ft)	441.96	442 ft.^{2}
(1.0034 in.)	(2.284 in.)	2.2917656	2.29 in.^{2}
(3.45 ft.)	(1.739 ft.)	5.99955	6.00 ft.^{2}
(87.9 yd.)	(123.8 yd.)	10882.02	10900 yd.^{2}

Figure 1-5.

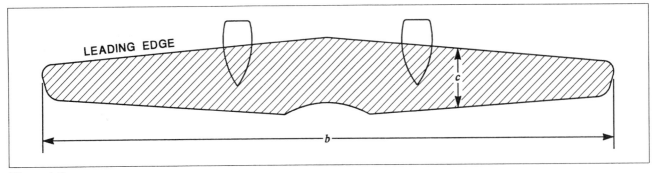

Figure 1-6.

$$AR = \frac{b}{c} = \frac{bb}{cb}$$

$$AR = \frac{b^2}{S}$$

In words, this formula tells us that the aspect ratio can be found by dividing the square of the span of the wing by the area of the wing.

Changing Units

One is often required to express a measurement written in the metric system to an equivalent unit in the English (engineering) system. Sometimes one must change an English or metric unit to an equivalent but smaller or larger unit. A table of "conversion factors" is essential for all of these unit changes. Figure 1-8 is a table of "conversion factors". Use this table for reference whenever you need to convert from one unit to another.

Note that any unit of length can be converted to any other unit of length. The same holds for area, volume, mass, force, speed, acceleration, pressure, time, energy, and power.

Suppose that a length is measured as 45.6m and you need to know this length in feet. The conversion can be done by looking up a conversion factor that relates these two units. Two different conversion factors can be found in the table.

$$1m = 3.281 \text{ ft.} \quad \text{or} \quad 1 \text{ ft.} = 0.0348m$$

Either of these conversion factors can be used. Study the following two calculations:

$$L = 45.6\,\cancel{m} \times \frac{3.281 \text{ ft.}}{1\,\cancel{m}} = 150 \text{ ft.}$$

Note that multiplication by the fraction is multiplication by a quantity equal to one (equal numerator and denominator). We put in the conversion in such a way that the unit that we do not want cancels out. We recall that we can cancel a unit in the numerator with the same unit in a denominator.

We could also have used the other conversion factor for our calculation.

$$L = 45.6\,\cancel{m} \times \frac{1 \text{ ft.}}{0.3048\,\cancel{m}} = 150 \text{ ft.}$$

This conversion factor also has a meter unit in the denominator. Also note that we multiplied in the first case since the 3.281 was in the numerator. In the second case, we divided by 0.3048 since this number was in the denominator.

Sometimes it is necessary to use several conversion factors to accomplish the necessary conversion.

Suppose we wish to change a mass of 3.78 slugs to grams. From our table, we note that there is no direct conversion factor. However, we see that the two conversion factors below will be needed.

$$1 \text{ slug} = 14.59 \text{ kg}$$
$$1{,}000 \text{ g} = 1 \text{ kg}$$

ORDINARY NOTATION	SCIENTIFIC NOTATION
45,000,000	4.50×10^7
0.000345	3.45×10^{-4}
350,000	3.50×10^5
0.0674	6.74×10^{-2}
12,000,000,000	1.20×10^{10}
0.00000783	7.83×10^{-6}

Figure 1-7.

TABLE OF CONVERSION FACTORS

LENGTH

1 in. = 2.54 cm

1 m = 9.37 in. = 3.281 ft.

1 ft. = 0.3048 m

12 in. = 1 ft.

3 ft. = 1 yd.

1 yd. = 0.9144 m

1 km = 0.621 mi.

1 mi. = 1.609 km = 5,280 ft.

AREA

$1 m^2$ = 0.76 $ft.^2$

$1 m^2$ = 10,000 cm^2

$1 ft.^2$ = 0.0929 m^2 = 144 $in.^2$

$1 in.^2$ = 6.452 cm^2

VOLUME

$1 m^3$ = 1,000,000 cm^3

$1 ft.^3$ = 1728 $in.^3$ = 0.0283 m^3

1 liter = 1000 cm^3 = 1.0576 qt.

$1 ft.^3$ = 7.481 gal.

1 gal. = 3.786 liters = 231 $in.^3$

MASS

1 amu = 1.66×10^{-27} kg

1000 kg = 1 metric ton

1000 g = 1 kg

1 slug = 14.59 kg

FORCE AND WEIGHT

1 N = 0.2248 lb.

1 lb. = 4.448 N

1 lb. = 16 oz.

VELOCITY

1 MPH = 1.47 ft./sec.

1 m/sec. = 3.281 ft./sec.

60 MPH = 88 ft./sec.

1 knot = 1.688 ft./sec.

1 knot = 1.151 MPH

1 knot = 1.852 km/hr.

1 MPH = 1.61 km/hr.

PRESSURE

1 atm = 76.0 cmHg

1 atm = 14.7 $lb./in.^2$

1 Pa = 0.000145 $lb./in.^2$

1 bar = 14.5 $lb./in.^2$

TIME

1 year = 365 days

1 day = 24 hr. = 1,440 min.

ENERGY

1 J = 0.738 ft. lb.

1 cal = 4.186 J

1 Btu = 252 cal.

POWER

1 HP = 550 ft. lb./sec.

1 HP = 0.746 kW

1 W = 1 J/sec.

1 W = 0.738 ft. lb./sec.

1 Btu/hr. = 0.293 W

FUNDAMENTAL CONSTANT

g = 32 lb./slug

= 9.8 N/kg

Figure 1-8.

We set up our conversion as follows:

$$m = 3.78 \text{ slugs} \times \frac{14.59 \text{ kg}}{1 \text{ slug}} \times \frac{1,000 \text{ g}}{1 \text{ kg}} = 55,200 \text{ g}$$

We see that the kilogram and slug units both cancel out. Note that we multiplied by both 14.59 and 1,000 since both of these numbers were in the numerator.

The answer could also be written 5.52×10^4. This form of notation is known as scientific nota-tion. The positive exponent tells us that the number written in ordinary notation can be found by moving the decimal in the first factor four places to the right.

Scientific notation can also be used to express very small numbers. In this case the exponent of ten is a negative number. This exponent tells us to move the decimal in the first factor to the left.

Study figure 1-7, a table of numbers written both in scientific notation and in ordinary notation.

Chapter I Problems

	WING SPAN	WING AREA	ASPECT RATIO
1.	12.4 m	21.3 m^2	_____
2.	43.41 m	268 m^2	_____
3.	11.2 m	16.4 m^2	_____
4.	84.0 ft.	4150 ft.^{2}	_____
5.	93.0 ft.	980 ft.^{2}	_____

	ORDINARY NOTATION	SCIENTIFIC NOTATION
6.	456,000	_____
7.	0.000457	_____
8.	23,700	_____
9.	_____	2.34×10^4
10.	_____	2.34×10^{-4}
11.	_____	4.90×10^2
12.	_____	7.82×10^{-5}

13. The wing span of a Learjet Model 24 is 10.84 meters. Express this wing span in feet.

14. The cabin door width of a Learjet Model 24 is 3.00 feet. Express this door width in meters.

15. The wing area for a Boeing 747 is 5,500 ft.^{2} Express this area in m^2.

16. The floor area of a Boeing 707-230 is 106 m^2. Express this area in ft.^{2}

17. Convert a speed of 45 MPH to ft./sec.

18. The Silver Sabre has a maximum rate of climb of 4,800 ft./min. Determine the rate of climb in ft./sec.

19. The maximum speed of a Piper Saratoga fitted with a three blade propeller is 152 knots. Calculate the speed in kilometers per hour.

20. The maximum speed of a Piper Seneca III is 196 knots. What is its speed in miles per hour?

21. Determine the number of seconds in 5.5 hours.

Chapter II

Matter, Mass, Force, Weight, Density, Pressure, and Temperature

Matter

Scientists for a long time suspected that all substances were composed of small particles which they called atoms. However, it wasn't until the beginning of this century that the existence of atoms was demonstrated to everyone's satisfaction. The size of the atom was found to be so small that a few hundred million, if placed side by side in a row, would form a line less than an inch long.

All atoms are, crudely speaking, the same size and can be thought to consist of two main parts. The outer part is a very sparse cloud which is composed of one or more electrons.

This cloud makes up most of the volume of the atom yet contributes practically nothing to its substance. The other part, located at the center, is extremely small compared to the atom as a whole, yet essentially all of the real substance of the atom can be attributed to this small speck. We call this speck the nucleus.

Further investigation revealed that the nucleus is actually composed of two kinds of particles of roughly equal size and substance packed closely together. These nuclear particles are the proton and neutron. When we refer to the amount of material or substance in an object, we are really talking about the number of protons and neutrons in that object. Also, what we perceive as the mass of an object is related directly to the number of protons and neutrons contained it. The simplest atom is hydrogen which has a single proton for a nucleus. An atom of lead, on the other hand, has 82 protons and 125 neutrons in its nucleus and so has 207 (125 + 82) times as much material or substance as an atom of hydrogen.

The size of an atom bears no simple relation to the number of particles in its nucleus. A sodium atom, for example, with 11 protons and 12 neutrons is approximately the same size as an atom of mercury with 80 protons and 121 neutrons.

Figure 2-2 shows a number of atoms drawn approximately to scale. Notice that the sizes are roughly the same even though the numbers of protons (P) and neutrons (N) vary appreciably.

In general, we can say that the size of an atom is determined by its electron cloud, its substance is determined by the total number of protons and neutrons in its nucleus.

Molecules

Atoms combine to form more complex structures which we call molecules. Like building blocks, these molecules organize to form all of the materials, solid, liquid and gas, which we encounter in our daily lives. Solids and liquids are materials in which the molecules attract one another so strongly that their relative motion is severely restricted. In a gas, the freedom of motion of the molecules is only slightly influenced by their mutual attraction. This is why gases fill the entire space to which they are confined. They spread out unconstrained until they encounter the walls of their container.

It is important to keep in mind that when we refer to the amount of gas in a container we are not talking about the volume of gas but the amount of material present which ultimately depends on the number of protons and neutrons in all the nuclei of all of the atoms of all of the molecules in that volume of gas.

Mass

In physics, the term for what we have up to now referred to as the amount of substance or matter is "mass". A natural unit for mass is the mass of a

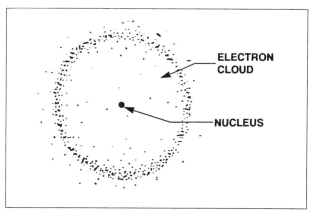

Figure 2-1.

proton or neutron. This unit has a special name, the "atomic mass unit" (amu). This unit is useful in those sciences which deal with atomic and nuclear matter.

In measuring the mass of objects which we encounter daily, this unit is much too small and therefore very inconvenient. For example, the mass of a bowling ball expressed in amu's would be about 4,380,000,000,000,000,000,000,000,000.

One kilogram equals 602,000,000,000,000,000, 000,000,000 amu. Since one amu is the mass of a proton or neutron we know immediately that a kilogram of anything has this combined number of protons and neutrons contained in it.

The kilogram is the standard unit of mass in the metric system. In the English system, the standard unit of mass is the slug.

The conversion is:

$$1 \text{ slug} = 14.59 \text{ kg} =$$
$$8,783,000,000,000,000,000,000,000,000 \text{ amu}$$

We will use the conveniently sized units, the slug in the English system and the kilogram in the metric system, for all of the problems that we will do in this course. Note that the above conversion, 1 slug = 14.59 kilogram, is listed with your conversion factors in the table of conversion factors (figure 1-8).

Force

The physicist uses the word "force" to describe any push or pull. A force is a one kind of vector. A vector is a quantity that has both size and direction.

A force has a certain magnitude or size. Also, a force is always in a certain direction. To completely describe a force, it is necessary to specify both the size of the push or pull and its direction.

The units in which force are measured are the pound (lb.) in the English system and the newton (N) in the metric system. The newton is named for Sir Isaac Newton, a famous British physicist who lived in the 17th century.

The relationship between the metric and English units is given by the conversion factor:

$$1 \text{ lb.} = 4.448 \text{ N}$$

This conversion is listed in your table of conversion factors (figure 1-8).

Weight

A weight is one kind of force. It is defined as the gravitational pull of the earth on a given body. The direction of this force is toward the geometrical center of the earth.

Distinction Between Mass and Weight

The physicist very carefully distinguishes between "mass" and "weight". As we have seen, mass is the quantity of matter, determined by the number of protons and neutrons in the body, and weight is a measure of the gravitational pull of the earth on this quantity of matter.

It may seem that this is an unimportant distinction. However, there is one important difference.

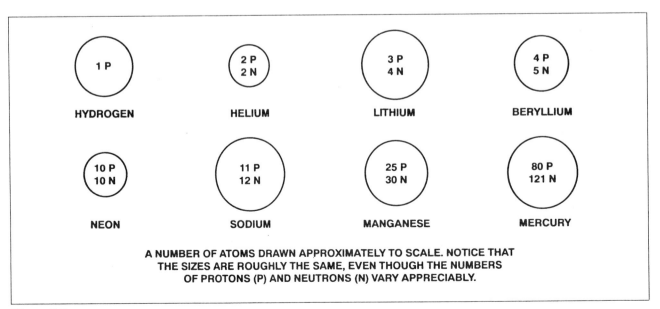

A NUMBER OF ATOMS DRAWN APPROXIMATELY TO SCALE. NOTICE THAT THE SIZES ARE ROUGHLY THE SAME, EVEN THOUGH THE NUMBERS OF PROTONS (P) AND NEUTRONS (N) VARY APPRECIABLY.

Figure 2-2.

DENSITIES OF LIQUIDS AND SOLIDS AT 68° FAHRENHEIT

	$\frac{kg}{m^3}$	$\frac{slug}{ft.^3}$		$\frac{kg}{m^3}$	$\frac{slug}{ft.^3}$
LIQUIDS			**METALS**		
Water	1,000	1.940	Aluminum	2,700	5.25
Sea Water	1,030	2.00	Cast Iron	7,200	14.0
Benzene	879	1.71	Copper	8,890	17.3
Ethyl Alcohol	789	1.53	Gold	19,300	37.5
Gasoline	680	1.32	Lead	11,340	22.0
Kerosene	800	1.55	Nickel	8,850	17.2
Lubricating Oil	900	1.75	Silver	10,500	20.4
Methyl Alcohol	792	1.54	Steel	7,800	15.1
Sulphuric Acid	1,831	3.55	Tungsten	19,000	37.0
Turpentine	873	1.69	Zinc	7,140	13.9
Mercury	13,595	26.38	Brass	8,700	16.9
NONMETALS			**WOODS**		
Ice (32°F)	922	1.79	Balsa	130	0.25
Concrete	2,300	4.48	Pine	480	0.93
Earth, Packed	1,500	2.92	Maple	640	1.24
Glass	2,600	4.97	Oak	720	1.40
Granite	2,700	5.25	Ebony	1,200	2.33

Figure 2-3.

The mass of an object is the same wherever this object is in the universe. The mass of a stone is the same if the stone is on the earth, on Mars, in a space ship, or some place in the Milky Way Galaxy. If the stone is not on the earth but is in a space station orbiting the earth some distance from the earth's surface, the weight of this stone is different from its weight on the earth's surface. If the stone is on the planet Mars, we speak of its "weight on Mars", the gravitational pull of Mars on the stone.

As you have probably figured out, the greater the mass of an object on the surface of the earth, the greater is the weight of this object. These two quantities are approximately proportional to each other as long as the body remains on the surface of the earth. The word "approximately" in the previous sentence refers to the fact that the pull of the earth on a body of a given mass varies slightly with the position of the body on the earth's surface. For example, a body that weighs 57.3 lbs. at the North Pole would weigh 57.0 lbs. at a place on the equator. This occurs because a body at either pole is slightly closer to the center of the earth than it is at the equator. Thus, the pull of the earth on the body is greater at the poles and slightly smaller at other places on the earth. However, we usually neglect this slight difference.

Physicists and engineers measure masses of bodies in slugs or kilograms and weights in pounds or newtons. The equation relating mass and weight is:

$$w = mg$$

In this equation, g has a definite numerical value. We will use the following relations:

$$g = 32 \frac{\text{lbs.}}{\text{slug}} \quad \text{or} \quad g = 9.8 \frac{\text{N}}{\text{kg}}$$

There is a great source of confusion in American marketing practices. For example, we often see on a box of corn flakes the information regarding the contents:

$$24 \text{ oz.} \quad \text{or} \quad 680 \text{ gms}$$

We note that 24 oz. equals 1.5 lbs. and 680 grams equals 0.68 kg. We have just learned that 1.5 lbs. is the weight of the corn flakes and that 0.68 kg is the mass of the corn flakes. In other words, American packaging practices list the weight of the product if we deal with the English system and list the mass of the product if we are in the metric system.

For example, suppose the weight of a piece of cheese is marked 32 oz. and we wish to know the number of grams. First we convert the weight in ounces to 2 lbs. Then we convert from pounds to newtons.

$$w = 2 \text{ lbs.} \times \frac{4.448 \text{ N}}{1 \text{ lb.}} = 8.90 \text{ N}$$

Next, we use the relation:

$$w = mg \quad \text{or} \quad m = \frac{w}{g}$$

Therefore, we write:

$$m = \frac{8.90 \text{ N}}{9.8 \text{ N/kg}} = 0.908 \text{ kg} = 908 \text{ grams}$$

Note that we can convert from pounds to newtons since both are units of weight and we can convert from kilograms to slugs since both are units of mass. However, if we want to find a mass if we know a weight or a weight if we know a mass we must use the equation:

$$m = w/g \quad \text{or} \quad w = mg$$

In summary, let us note that mass is a measure of the quantity of matter — ultimately, a measure of the number of protons and neutrons in the body and weight is the force with which the earth pulls on a body. These are related but not identical concepts. The units of mass are slugs and kilograms. The units of weight are pounds and newtons. A mass can be changed from slugs to kilograms and vice versa. A weight can be changed from newtons to pounds or vice versa. However, one **cannot** say that one pound **equals** 454 grams. The only correct statement is that a body having a **weight** of one pound has a **mass** of 454 grams. The equation relating mass and weight is:

$$w = mg \quad \text{or} \quad m = \frac{w}{g}$$

Density

The density of a type of material is defined as the mass of a sample of the material divided by the volume of the same sample. The symbol used for density is the Greek letter rho, (ρ).

$$\rho = \frac{m}{V}$$

Other algebraic forms of this same equation are:

$$m = \rho V \quad \text{and} \quad V = \frac{m}{\rho}$$

Density is a very important and useful concept. If a body is made of a certain kind of material its density is known. If the weight of the body is also known, it is possible to determine the volume of this body. Similarly, if the kind of material and volume are known it is possible to determine the weight of the body.

A table of densities is shown in figure 2-3. You can refer to this table when you solve the problems dealing with mass, weight, and volume.

EXAMPLE 2-A.

An order has been placed for 120 gal. of lubricating oil. How much will this oil weigh?

$$V = 120 \text{ gal.} \times \frac{1 \text{ ft.}^3}{7.481 \text{ gal.}} = 16.0 \text{ ft.}^3$$

$$\rho = 1.75 \frac{\text{slug}}{\text{ft.}^3}$$

The density of the lubricating oil has been obtained from figure 2-3.

$$m = \rho V$$

$$m = \left(\frac{1.75 \text{ slugs}}{\cancel{\text{ft.}}^3}\right)(16.0 \ \cancel{\text{ft.}}^3) = 28 \text{ slugs}$$

$$w = mg = (28 \ \cancel{\text{slugs}})\left(\frac{32 \text{ lbs.}}{\cancel{\text{slug}}}\right) = 896 \text{ lbs.}$$

EXAMPLE 2-B.

An order has been placed for 150 lbs. of turpentine. How many gallons of turpentine will be delivered?

$$m = \frac{w}{g} = \frac{150 \ \cancel{\text{lbs.}}}{32 \ \cancel{\text{lbs.}}/\text{slug}} = 4.69 \text{ slug}$$

$$V = \frac{m}{\rho} = \frac{4.69 \ \cancel{\text{slug}}}{1.69 \ \cancel{\text{slug}}/\text{ft.}} = 2.78 \text{ ft.}$$

$$V = 2.78 \ \cancel{\text{ft.}} \times \frac{7.481 \text{ gal.}}{1 \ \cancel{\text{ft.}}} = 20.8 \text{ gal.}$$

Specific Gravity

The term "specific gravity" is closely related to the idea of density. The definition is as follows:

$$\text{Specific Gravity} = \frac{\text{density of the substance}}{\text{density of water}}$$

The calculation will give the same result (for a given substance) no matter what units are used. The example below will calculate the specific gravity of sulfuric acid (see figure 2-3).

If we use the metric units (kg/m^3) we obtain:

$$\text{Specific Gravity} = \frac{1,831}{1,000} = 1.83$$

If we use the English units ($slug/ft.^3$) we obtain:

$$\text{Specific Gravity} = \frac{3.55}{1.94} = 1.83$$

The specific gravity number (1.83) is unitless. It tells us that, for sulfuric acid, the density is 1.83 times as dense as water.

Pressure

Pressure is defined as the force divided by the area on which the force acts. The equation defining pressure is:

$$P = \frac{F}{A}$$

Another form of this equation is:

$$F = PA$$

EXAMPLE 2-C.

On a day when the atmospheric pressure is 14.8 lbs./in.^{2}, what is the force acting on a desk top having an area of 240 in.^{2}?

$$F = PA = 14.8 \ \frac{\text{lbs.}}{\cancel{\text{in.}}^2} \times 240 \ \cancel{\text{in.}}^2 = 3,550 \text{ lbs.}$$

The molecules making up a gas are in ceaseless motion. They collide and rebound from any solid surface which they encounter. These collisions result in a net push or force on the surface. As we have said, this force, divided by the area of the surface over which it is exerted, is called pressure.

Gas molecules colliding with the walls of their container exert an average force per unit area (see figure 2-4).

The metric unit of pressure is the N/m^2 (newton per square meter) which is less than the pressure a sheet exerts on you while you lie in bed. This pressure ($1 \ N/m^2$) has been named the pascal (Pa)

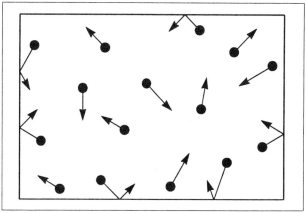

Figure 2-4.

in honor of the French scientist and mathematician, Blaise Pascal, who did much to advance our knowledge of fluids. The pascal is a very small unit of pressure and because of this gas pressures, which are ordinarily encountered, are expressed in thousands of pascals or kilopascals (kPa). For example, normal atmospheric pressure is nearly 101 kPa. Another unit just about equal to normal atmospheric pressure is the bar. One bar is defined to be 100 kPa.

The English unit of pressure is the lb./ft.^{2} or the lb./in.^{2} (PSI). Another unit of pressure is the atmosphere (atm) which equals 14.7 lbs./in.^{2}

Atmospheric Pressure

On our earth, we live under a blanket of air. As we will see in chapter 4, the density of air decreases with altitude. At sea level, the average atmospheric pressure is 14.7 lbs./in.^{2} Various types of barometers are used to measure atmospheric pressure.

The mercury barometer is a narrow vertical glass tube which is inverted in a dish of mercury. The small space above the mercury column is a perfect vacuum. As the air molecules bombard the surface of the mercury in the dish, they balance the mercury in the column since there are **no** bombarding molecules above the mercury in the column. The height of the mercury column varies slightly from day to day as the atmospheric pressure changes. At standard pressure (14.7 lbs./in.^{2}) the mercury column is 760 millimeters high. In the English system the height of the mercury column is 29.92 inches. Sometimes we use the height of mercury (Hg) column as a unit for stating pressure.

Thus, we can say:

$$1 \text{ Atmosphere} = 14.7 \text{ lb./in.}^2$$
$$= 760 \text{ mmHg} = 29.92 \text{ in.Hg}$$

It seems strange that we sometimes state a pressure by giving a distance (the height of the Hg column), but it is standard practice for TV weather commentators! Note that a weather commentator will tell us, for example, that the pressure on a certain day is 29.3.

Absolute Pressure and Gage Pressure

All of the pressure measuring instruments which the airplane mechanic is likely to use are designed to register the extent to which the pressure being measured differs from the ambient pressure. The term "ambient pressure" refers to the pressure in the area immediately surrounding the object under study. For example, a tire gage registering 32.0 lbs./in.^{2} is telling us that the pressure inside the tire is 32.0 lbs./in.^{2} greater than the pressure outside the tire. On a day when the atmospheric pressure is 14.6 lbs./in.^{2}, the actual pressure the gas is exerting on the inner walls of the tire is 46.6 lbs./in.^{2} (32.0 + 14.6).

The actual pressure the gas is exerting on the walls of its container is called the absolute pressure. The general relation which connects gage pressure, absolute pressure and atmospheric pressure is:

$$P_{abs} = P_g + P_{atm}$$

The zero on the absolute pressure scale is the pressure exerted by a perfect vacuum.

Let us assume that the atmospheric pressure on a certain day is 15 lbs./in.^{2} Figure 2-5 is a chart giving the gage pressure and the absolute pressure for several different examples.

Note that the equation $P_{abs} = P_g + P_{atm}$ is satisfied in each entry in the chart.

Temperature

Our common notion of hot and cold has its precise expression in the concept of temperature. As objects are heated their molecules move faster. In a solid, the molecules vibrate more rapidly. In liquids and gases the molecules move all over in the container at a faster rate of speed. These variations in speed of the molecules cause objects to expand when they are heated.

This expansion can be used to construct instruments called thermometers. The ordinary mercury thermometer uses the expansion of a volume of mercury contained in a bulb to indicate temperature.

	ABSOLUTE PRESSURE (LB./IN.^{2})	GAGE PRESSURE (LB./IN.^{2})
Inside a Tire	49	34
Pressure Cooker	35	20
Outside Air	15	0
Cabin Pressure of a Plane	11	– 4
Perfect Vacuum	0	–15

Figure 2-5.

A number of temperature scales are currently in use. The Fahrenheit scale is the one we have used most extensively. On this scale the freezing point of water is 32° and its boiling point is 212°. The metric scale is the Celsius or centigrade scale. On this scale the freezing point of water is zero and the boiling point is 100°.

In theory, if we cool any substance enough, we can cause all molecular motion to cease. We call this lowest possible temperature "absolute zero". Ordinary gases like air would be rock solid at this temperature. Low temperature physicists have never been able to reach this extremely low temperature in their laboratories. However, they have come close—down to a fraction of a centigrade degree. Absolute zero is a limiting temperature which can never be reached. Two other temperature scales are used by engineers and experimental scientists. In both of these scales the zero of the scale is placed at absolute zero, the coldest possible temperature. These scales are the metric Kelvin scale and the English Rankine scale.

In figure 2-6, the four temperature scales are compared.

There are formulas that enable us to change from a centigrade reading to a Fahrenheit reading and vice versa. These formulas are:

$$C = \frac{5}{9}(F - 32) \qquad \text{and} \qquad F = \frac{9}{5}C + 32$$

Note that there are parentheses in the first formula but not in the second formula. Be careful!

You have probably already used these two formulas in other classes. You will be given an opportunity to practice their use in the problems that follow.

There are also formulas that change from a centigrade reading to a Kelvin reading and from a Fahrenheit reading to a Rankine reading. These formulas are very important to us at this time since we will have to use absolute temperatures in the gas laws which follow in chapter 3.

These formulas are:

$$K = C + 273 \qquad \text{and} \qquad R = F + 460$$

Note that these formulas are verified in the comparison chart (figure 2-6).

	BOILING POINT OF WATER	FREEZING POINT OF WATER	ABSOLUTE ZERO
Centigrade	100°	0°	−273°
Kelvin	373°	273°	0°
Fahrenheit	212°	32°	−460°
Rankine	672°	492°	0°

Figure 2-6.

Chapter II Problems

1. What is the mass of a body having a weight of 45 N?

2. What is the weight of a body having a mass of 23 kg?

3. What is the mass of a body having a weight of 350 lbs.?

4. What is the weight of a body having a mass of 23.6 slugs?

5. What is the weight of the corn flakes in a box where the mass is listed as 680 g?

6. What is the mass in grams of 2.5 lbs. of bologna?

7. What is the weight of 85 gallons of kerosene?

8. How many gallons of benzene will be delivered if 125 lbs. of this liquid are ordered?

9. What is the weight of 3,000 gallons gasoline?

10. What is the volume (in gallons) of 3,500 lbs. of water?

11. What is the specific gravity of kerosene?

12. What is the specific gravity of aluminum?

13. What is the specific gravity of ice?

14. What is the specific gravity of glass?

15. On a day when the barometric (or atmospheric) pressure is 14.9 lbs./in.^{2} and the pressure gage on a tire reads 34.6 lbs./in.^{2}, what is the absolute pressure inside this tire?

16. If the absolute pressure inside a tire is 55.0 lbs./in.^{2} and the pressure gage reads 40.3 lbs./in.^{2}, what is the atmospheric pressure?

17. If the atmospheric pressure is 14.5 lbs./in.^{2} and the absolute pressure is 67.0 lbs./in.^{2}, what is the gage pressure?

18. Change 20 °C to degrees F.

19. Change –15 °C to degrees F.

20. Change 86 °F to degrees C.

21. Change –4°F to degrees C.

22. Change 100 °F to degrees R.

23. Change 450 °R to degrees F.

24. Change 100 °C to degrees K.

25. Change 383 °K to degrees C.

26. Gas turbine engine performance is very sensitive to variations in the temperature of the air. All engines are rated with the air at a standard temperature of 59 °F. What is the equivalent Centigrade temperature?

27. On some large commercial turbojet engines, the temperature at the front end of the combustion section is approximately 400 °C. What is this temperature on the Fahrenheit scale?

28. As air enters the combustion chamber of a turbojet, fuel is added and the temperature is raised to about 3,500 °F in the hottest part of the flame. What is this temperature on the Centigrade scale?

Chapter III

The Gas Laws

We will next discuss the volume and density of gases under varying conditions of temperature and pressure. Three gas laws, named after the scientists that discovered them, will be considered.

Boyle's Law

A cylinder containing gas is fitted with a tight piston. This cylinder contains a certain mass of gas, and therefore a certain number of molecules of gas. The gas has a definite absolute temperature. This temperature is a measure of the average speed of the gas molecules in the sample. Some of the molecules are moving faster and some are moving slower. The average speed determines the temperature.

If the temperature of the gas remains constant and the volume of the gas sample is decreased, the molecules, still moving with the same average speed, are "squashed" into a smaller space (see figure 3-1).

The result is that the sides of the container experience more collisions per unit time. This results in an increase in the absolute pressure the molecules exert on the walls of the container.

Note that a decrease in volume produces an increase in absolute pressure. This is characteristic of an inverse proportion. We write the equation as:

$$\frac{P_1}{P_2} = \frac{V_2}{V_1}$$

If we cross multiply in the above equation we reach the form in which Boyle's Law is usually written:

$$P_1 V_1 = P_2 V_2$$

Here P_1 and P_2 are the absolute pressures corresponding to the volumes V_1 and V_2 respectively. In working with Boyle's Law, it must always be remembered to use absolute pressures.

EXAMPLE 3-A.

A cylinder fitted with a piston contains gas at a pressure of 35.5 lbs./in.^{2} as indicated by a gage mounted to the outside of the cylinder. The atmospheric pressure is 14.5 lbs./in.^{2} If the piston is forced down reducing the volume in the cylinder to one fourth of its original volume while holding the temperature of the gas constant, determine the new reading on the pressure gage.

$$P_1 = (35.5 + 14.5) \text{ lbs./in.}^2$$

$$P_1 = 50 \text{ lbs./in.}^2$$

$$V_2 = \frac{1}{4} V_1$$

$$P_1 V_1 = P_2 V_2$$

$$(50 \text{ lbs./in.}^2) (V_1) = P_2 (\frac{1}{4} V_1)$$

Solving for P_2 gives,

$$P_2 = 200 \text{ lbs./in.}^2 \text{ absolute}$$

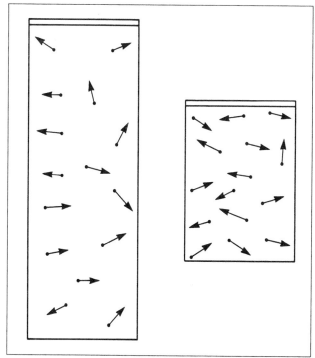

Figure 3-1.

We still must express this new pressure as a gage pressure since the problem asked for the new reading on the pressure gage. Our final answer is:

$$P_2 = (200 - 14.5) \text{ lbs./in.}^2 = 186 \text{ lbs./in.}^2$$

Charles' Law

Toward the end of the 18th century, investigations carried out by French physicists, Jacques Alexandre Charles and Joseph Louis Gay-Lussac, led to the discovery of a relation between the volume and absolute temperature of gases under conditions of constant pressure.

Let us again consider a sample of gas containing a definite number of molecules. We stipulate that the pressure on this sample of gas will remain constant. If the pressure is to remain constant, an increase in absolute temperature must be accompanied by a corresponding increase in volume (see figure 3-2).

We say that the volume is directly proportional to the absolute temperature, provided that the pressure remains constant. We write the equation as:

$$\frac{V_1}{T_1} = \frac{V_2}{T_2}$$

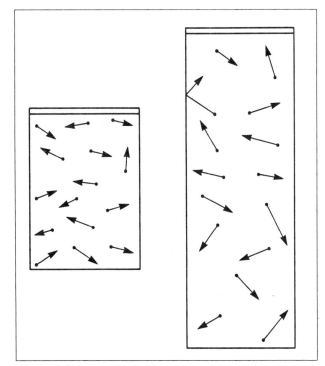

Figure 3-2.

The absolute temperatures can be either Kelvin degrees or Rankine degrees.

EXAMPLE 3-B.

A quantity of air occupies a volume of one cubic foot on a day when the temperature is 15°F. What will be the volume of this quantity of air when the temperature increases to 85°F, and the pressure stays the same?

$$\frac{1 \text{ ft.}^3}{475 \text{ R}°} = \frac{V_2}{545 \text{ R}°}$$

Note that we have changed the temperatures from degrees Fahrenheit to degrees Rankine, because we must express the temperatures in absolute units.

Cross multiplying, we obtain:

$$V_2 = \frac{1 \text{ ft.}^3 \times 545 \text{ R}°}{475 \text{ R}°} = 1.15 \text{ ft.}^3$$

Failure to convert to absolute temperatures will always lead to incorrect answers when working with the gas laws!

Gay-Lussac's Law

This third gas law relates the absolute pressure to the absolute temperature of a gas when its volume is held constant.

Again we consider a certain number of molecules of gas in a closed container where the volume of the gas is held constant. If we increase the absolute temperature of the gas, the average speed of the molecules increases. As these molecules strike the walls of the container they exert a greater pressure since they are moving faster (see figure 3-3).

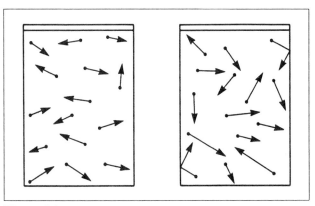

Figure 3-3.

Using absolute pressures and temperatures the following simple relationship is obtained:

$$\frac{P_1}{T_1} = \frac{P_2}{T_2}$$

This equation is referred to as Gay-Lussac's Law.

EXAMPLE 3-C.

The tire of a bicycle is filled with air to a gage pressure of 50.0 lbs./in. at 58°C. What is the gage pressure in the tire on a day when the temperature rises to 86°C? Assume that the volume of the tire does not change and the atmospheric pressure is 14.7 lbs./in.^{2}

We must first convert to absolute temperatures and pressures.

P_1 = 50.0 lbs./in.^{2} + 14.7 lbs./in.^{2} = 64.7 lbs./in.^{2}

T_1 = 460° + 58° = 518°R

T_2 = 460° + 86° = 546°R

Substituting these values into Gay-Lussac's Law gives:

$$\frac{64.7 \text{ lbs./in.}^2}{518°R} = \frac{P_2}{546°R}$$

Solving for P_2, we obtain P_2 = 68.2 lbs./in.^{2}

Finally, the new gage pressure is obtained by subtracting the atmospheric pressure from P_2.

68.2 lbs./in.^{2} − 14.7 lbs./in.^{2} = 53.5 lbs./in.^{2}

The General Gas Law

The three properties, pressure, temperature, and volume are interrelated for a fixed mass (number of molecules) of gas in such a way that if two of them change in value the third can immediately be determined. Combining the three gas laws the following general gas law can be written:

$$\frac{P_1 V_1}{T_1} = \frac{P_2 V_2}{T_2}$$

Note that this equation gives us the three gas laws that we have studied.

If the temperature of the gas remains constant, we can cancel the temperatures in the denominators and obtain:

$$P_1 V_1 = P_2 V_2 \qquad \text{Boyle's Law}$$

If the pressure remains constant, we can cancel the pressures in the numerators and obtain:

$$\frac{V_1}{T_1} = \frac{V_2}{T_2} \qquad \text{Charles' Law}$$

If the volume remains constant, we can cancel the volumes in the numerators and obtain:

$$\frac{P_1}{T_1} = \frac{P_2}{T_2} \qquad \text{Gay-Lussac's Law}$$

EXAMPLE 3-D.

A tank of helium gas has a gage pressure of 50.2 lbs./in.^{2} and a temperature of 45°F. A piston decreases the volume of the gas to 68% of its original volume and the temperature drops to 10°F. What is the new gage pressure? Assume normal atmospheric pressure.

We must change both temperatures to absolute units. We must change the original gage pressure to absolute pressure. We remember that when the final pressure is obtained it will be in absolute units. We also note that $V_2 = 0.68\ V_1$.

$$\frac{P_1 V_1}{T_1} = \frac{P_2 V_2}{T_2}$$

We transfer V_2 from the numerator on the right to the denominator on the left. We also transfer T_2 from the denominator on the right to the numerator on the left. In this way, we solve our formula for P_2..

$$\frac{P_1 V_1 T_2}{T_1 V_2} = P_2$$

Next we substitute our known values:

$$P_2 = \frac{(64.9 \text{ lbs./in.}^2)\ (V_1)\ (470°R)}{(505°R)\ (0.68\ V_1)}$$

$$P_2 = 88.8 \text{ lbs./in.}^2 \text{ Absolute}$$

$$P_2 = 74.1 \text{ lbs./in.}^2 \text{ (New Gage Pressure)}$$

Alternate Form of the General Gas Law

The general gas law tells us that for a fixed quantity of gas, the expression PV/T is constant. Since PV/T is a constant for a fixed mass of gas, we can set this expression equal to the product of the mass (m) of the gas and what is referred to as a gas constant (R). This gas constant (R) varies according to the type of gas. A table giving values of R for various gases can be found in figure 3-4.

We can write:

$$\frac{PV}{T} = mR$$

$$PV = mRT$$

If we divide both sides of this equation by V, we obtain:

$$P = \frac{mRT}{V}$$

We remember that the density of any substance is given by:

$$\rho = \frac{m}{V}$$

VALUES OF THE GAS CONSTANT, R, FOR SOME COMMON GASES		
	kPa m^3/kg K$^\circ$	ft. lb./slug R$^\circ$
Air	0.287	1710
Carbon Dioxide	0.189	1130
Helium	2.077	12,380
Nitrogen	0.297	1770
Oxygen	0.260	1550
Water Vapor	0.462	2760

Figure 3-4.

Therefore we can write:

$$P = \rho RT$$

The most important application of this formula enables us to obtain the density of any particular kind of gas if we know its absolute pressure and absolute temperature.

We write the equation in the form:

$$\rho = \frac{P}{RT}$$

EXAMPLE 3-E.

Find the density of air if the temperature is 80°F and the absolute pressure is 2,150 lbs./ft.^{2}

$$\rho = \frac{P}{RT} = \frac{2150 \text{ lbs./ft.}^2}{(1710 \text{ ft. lbs./slug R}^\circ)(540 \text{ R}^\circ)}$$

$$= 0.00233 \text{ slug/ft.}^3$$

Application of the General Gas Law to Compressors

We can apply the general gas law to the flow of air through the compressor of a turbojet engine. The function of the compressor is to provide a large quantity of high pressure air to the **limited space of the combustion chamber**. The reason for this is that the energy released in the combustion chamber is proportional to the mass of air consumed. The pressure of the air when it leaves the compressor is called the compressor discharge pressure (CDP) and the ratio of this to the compressor inlet pressure (CIP) is the compression ratio. That is,

$$\text{Compression Ratio} = \frac{CDP}{CIP}$$

Note that the compression ratio can also be expressed as:

$$\text{Compression Ratio} = \frac{P_2}{P_1}$$

where the 1's refer to the inlet pressure and the 2's to the discharge pressure.

Air entering a compressor having a compression ratio of 12.5:1 at a pressure of 14.7 PSIA will leave with a pressure of:

$$(12.5)\ (14.7) = 184\ \text{PSIA}$$

If, however, the temperature of the air is increased too much in the compression process the volume of a quantity of air entering the combustion chamber will not be reduced significantly and the compressor efficiency will be low.

EXAMPLE 3-F.

A quantity of air occupying 1 cu. ft. at a pressure of 14.7 PSIA and a temperature of 59°F enters the compressor of a turbojet engine having a compression ratio of 12.5:1 and is discharged at a temperature of 2,000°F. With what volume will this quantity of air enter the combustion chamber?

Solving our general equation:

$$\frac{P_1 V_1}{T_1} = \frac{P_2 V_2}{T_2} \quad \text{for } V_2 \text{ yields}$$

$$V_2 = \frac{P_1 V_1 T_2}{T_1 P_2} = V_1 \left(\frac{T_2}{T_1}\right) \left(\frac{1}{P_2/P_1}\right)$$

Therefore, we can substitute our given values:

$$V_2 = \left(1\ \text{ft.}^3\right) \left(\frac{2,000 + 460}{59 + 460}\right) \left(\frac{1}{12.5}\right)$$

$$V_2 = 0.379\ \text{ft.}^3$$

EXAMPLE 3-G.

With what volume would the quantity of air of the previous problem enter the combustion chamber if the discharge temperature of the compressor were 750°F instead of 2,000°F?

$$V^2 = \left(1\ \text{ft.}^3\right) \left(\frac{750 + 460}{59 + 460}\right) \left(\frac{1}{12.5}\right)$$

$$V^2 = 0.187\ \text{ft.}^3$$

We see that the volume of the original cubic foot of air is less (0.187 ft.^{3}) when the temperature is 750°F than it is (0.379 ft.^{3}) when the temperature is 2,000°F.

Because of the limited space of the combustion chamber, it is important that the volume be lower. Therefore, the temperature of the air in the compression chamber must not be increased too much.

Chapter III Problems

1. A quantity of gas is contained in a cylinder fitted with a piston. The absolute pressure of the gas is 240 kPa when the volume is 0.15 m³. What will the volume be when the absolute pressure of the gas is changed to 80 kPa while the temperature is held constant?

2. A quantity of gas is contained in a cylinder fitted with a piston. The gage pressure of the gas in the cylinder is 335 lbs./in.² when the volume occupied by the gas is 72 in.³ What is the gage pressure when the volume is decreased to 60 in.³? Assume atmospheric pressure to be 15 lbs./in.², and assume that the temperature is held constant.

3. A tank of carbon dioxide has a gage pressure of 32.0 lbs./in.² and a volume of 4.5 ft.³ Care is taken that the temperature remains the same as the volume is gradually reduced with a tight-fitting piston. When the volume has been reduced to 2.3 ft.³ what is the new gage pressure? Assume standard atmospheric pressure, 14.7 lbs./in.²

4. The volume of acetylene in a tank with a tight-fitting piston is 5.70 ft.³ The gage pressure is 28.2 lbs./in.² The volume of the tank is increased until the new gage pressure is 20.0 lbs./in.² What is the new volume of the acetylene in the tank? Assume that the temperature remains the same as the volume is increased and that there is standard atmospheric pressure.

5. A sample of nitrogen is held at an absolute pressure of 1.50 atmospheres and a volume of 7.80 m³. A piston gradually reduces the volume to 6.30 m³. The temperature does not change. What is the new absolute pressure in atmospheres?

6. A volume of 1.35 m³ of air at 17 °C is heated to 427 °C while its pressure is held constant. What is the volume of the gas at this elevated temperature?

7. Gas is contained in a cylinder fitted with a piston. The gas pressure is held constant by a weight resting on the piston. Initially, the volume of the gas is 75 in.³ and its temperature is 515 °F. The cylinder is then cooled causing the volume to decrease to 25 in.³ What is the temperature of the gas corresponding to this volume?

8. A filled tank of carbon dioxide has a gage pressure of 45.0 lbs./in.² when the temperature is 58 °F. The temperature increases to 102°F on a very hot day. What is the new gage pressure? Assume that the atmospheric pressure is the standard 14.7 lbs./in.²

9. A nosewheel tire is filled to a gage pressure of 105.8 lbs./in.² when the atmospheric pressure is 14.7 lbs./in.² and the temperature is 85 °F. The temperature decreases to 45 °F (as a cold front comes in) and atmospheric pressure decreases to 13.9 lbs./in.² Find the gage pressure under these new conditions of temperature and atmospheric pressure. Assume that the volume of the tire remains constant.

10. A dirigible is filled with helium gas. The volume of the balloon is 25,700 ft.³, the absolute pressure is 14.9 lbs./in.² and the temperature is 87 °F. The balloon later experiences an absolute pressure 14.1 lbs./in.² and simultaneously a temperature of 45 °F. What is the new volume of this balloon?

11. A tank is fitted with a tight piston. The gage pressure is 68.0 lbs./in.² If the temperature remains constant and the piston is moved so that the new volume is 35% of the original volume, what is the new gage pressure? Assume standard atmospheric pressure.

12. A rubber helium balloon is purchased in a floral shop on a hot summer day when the temperature in the air conditioned shop is 71 °F. The volume of the balloon is 0.354 ft.³ in the shop. The balloon is carried into a car overheated by the greenhouse effect to a temperature of 120 °F. Assume the pressure remains the same. The balloon is seen to "puff out". What is the new volume of the balloon?

13. A tank of carbon dioxide is maintained at an absolute pressure of 5,550 lbs./ft.² The temperature is 195 °F. What is the density of this carbon dioxide?

14. The air pressure and density at a point on the wing of a Boeing 747 flying at an altitude of 2900 m are 71.0 kPa, and 0.919 kg/m³ respectively. What is the temperature at this point on the wing in degrees Centigrade?

15. The Goodyear non-rigid airship, the Mayflower, has a volume of $4174\ m^3$ and is filled with helium to an absolute pressure of 101.4 kPa. The temperature is 27 °C. Find the density and total mass of the helium in the ship.

16. At an altitude of 8,000 ft. the absolute temperature of air is 490 °R and the absolute pressure is 1572 lbs./ft.^{2} What is the density of air at this altitude?

17. A dirigible is filled with helium gas. The volume of the balloon is 25,700 ft.^{3} when the absolute pressure is 14.9 lbs./in.^{2} and the temperature is 87 °F. The balloon later experiences an absolute pressure of 13.9 lbs./in.^{2} and simultaneously a temperature of 25 °F. What is the new volume of this balloon?

18. The volume of a "happy birthday" balloon is 0.950 ft.^{3} in a floral shop where the temperature is 70 °F. The balloon is carried to an overheated car where the temperature is 102 °F. What is the new volume of the balloon? Assume the pressure remains constant.

19. A tank of carbon dioxide is maintained at an absolute pressure of 4,500 lbs./ft.^{2} and a temperature of 70 °F. What is the density of this carbon dioxide?

20. A quantity of air occupying 0.9 ft.^{3} at a pressure of 14.7 PSIA and a temperature of 40 °F enters the compressor of a turbojet engine having a compression ratio of 13:1 and is discharged at a temperature of 1,900 °F. With what volume will this quantity of air enter the combustion chamber?

21. In the preceding problem, what will be the volume if the discharge temperature is 700 °F?

Chapter IV

The Atmosphere

On November 21, 1783, a hot air balloon carrying Marquis d'Arlandes, flew 5 miles across the skies of Paris opening up new possibilities in travel and a fresh interest in our atmosphere. It wasn't, however, until heavier-than-air flight became a reality that a detailed understanding of the medium enveloping our globe became essential.

The atmosphere is a mixture of gases which we call air. Dry air is composed of approximately 21% oxygen, 78% nitrogen, and 1% carbon dioxide. These percentages remain fairly constant as we ascend in altitude. However, the density of air decreases. This drop in density with altitude has great significance in aviation as it not only places limits on the attainable altitudes, but also the powerplant performance of an aircraft.

The mapping out of our atmosphere, that is, determining its density, pressure, and temperature at different altitudes, required the effort of many individuals working over many years. The fruit of this labor is a vast quantity of data which has led to the definition of a standard atmosphere. The standard atmosphere, a term coined by Willis Ray Gregg in 1922, is a compilation of mean annual atmospheric properties. Since our atmosphere undergoes seasonal variations in properties such as temperature, a mean or average value is used. Figures 4-1 and 4-2 are two tables of values for the standard atmosphere. The first table (figure 4-1) gives values in English units and the second (figure 4-2) in metric units. It must be kept in mind that the numbers in these tables are annual averages which can be useful for reference purposes but do not indicate the actual atmospheric conditions existing at any particular moment.

EXAMPLE 4-A.

Using the Gas Law and the temperature and pressure at an altitude of 12,000 meters listed in the Standard Atmosphere Table (figure 4-2), verify that the density of air at this altitude is 0.312 kg/m^3.

We will use the equation $\rho = P/RT$.

$$\rho = \frac{19.4 \text{ kPa}}{(0.287 \text{ kPa·m}^3/\text{kg °K})(217°K)}$$

$$= 0.312 \text{ kg/m}^3$$

Cabin Altitude

Cabin altitude is a term used to express cabin pressure in terms of equivalent altitude above sea level. For example, a cabin altitude of 6,000 feet means that the pressure inside the airplane cabin is the same as the atmospheric pressure at an altitude of 6,000 feet. Looking at the Standard Atmosphere Table (figure 4-1), the pressure is found to be 1,696 lbs./ft.^{2} which upon division by 144 gives the pressure in lb./in.^{2} to be 11.78 lbs./in.^{2}

At a cabin altitude of 8,000 feet, the passengers and crew can ride in relative comfort without any special oxygen supply. Planes which fly at much higher altitudes than 8,000 feet must be furnished with a special atmosphere control system. It is highly advantageous to fly at high altitudes both for economy of fuel consumption, and the smooth air high above the level of turbulent weather systems. At these high altitudes, the pressure outside the plane can be significantly lower than the cabin pressure.

At 8,000 ft., the Standard Atmosphere Table tells us that the air pressure is 1,572 lbs./ft.^{2} or 10.92 lbs./in.^{2} This is the pressure that is normally maintained in the cabin even though the plane is flying at a higher altitude.

Suppose the plane is flying at an altitude of 40,000 ft. At this altitude the pressure (from the figure 4-1) is 393 lbs./ft.^{2} or 2.73 lbs./in.^{2} This means that for a cabin altitude of 8,000 ft. for a plane flying at 40,000 ft., there is a net outward pressure of 8.19 lbs./in.^{2} This number was obtained by subtracting 2.73 lbs./in.^{2} from 10.92. For a Learjet 24d with a pressurized area of 45,000 in.^{2}, we are dealing with a bursting force of over 368,000 lbs. (8.19 × 45 thousand). In addition to being able to withstand this much force, a safety factor of 1.33 is generally used by design engineers. Therefore, the pressurized portion of the fuselage must be constructed to have an ultimate strength of over 460 thousand pounds or about 230 tons! The challenge of finding light weight materials which can withstand these large forces is great.

In the description of an airplane's air conditioning and pressurization system, a differential pressure is given. The differential pressure is the maximum difference between cabin pressure and atmospheric pressure which the pressurization system can sustain. For example, the air-cycle air-conditioning system of a Boeing 747 can maintain a pressure differential of 8.9 lbs./in.^{2} This means that the system can maintain a cabin pressure 8.9 lbs./in.^{2} greater than the atmospheric pressure surrounding the plane. This also means that there is an upper limit imposed by the pressurization system on the altitude at which the plane can fly.

STANDARD ATMOSPHERE – ENGLISH UNITS			
ALTITUDE (FT.)	TEMPERATURE (°R)	PRESSURE (LB./FT.^{2})	DENSITY (SLUG/FT.^{3})
0	519	2,116	0.002377
500	517	2,078	0.002342
1,000	515	2,041	0.002308
2,000	512	1,968	0.002241
3,000	508	1,897	0.002175
4,000	504	1,828	0.002111
5,000	501	1,761	0.002048
6,000	497	1,696	0.001987
7,000	494	1,633	0.001927
8,000	490	1,572	0.001869
9,000	487	1,513	0.001811
10,000	484	1,456	0.001756
15,000	465	1,195	0.001496
20,000	447	973	0.001267
25,000	430	786	0.001066
30,000	412	630	0.000891
35,000	394	499	0.000738
40,000	390	393	0.000585
45,000	390	309	0.000462
50,000	390	244	0.000364
55,000	390	192	0.000287
60,000	390	151	0.000226
65,000	390	119	0.000178

Figure 4-1.

STANDARD ATMOSPHERE – METRIC UNITS			
ALTITUDE (METERS)	TEMPERATURE ($^\circ$K)	PRESSURE (kPa)	DENSITY (kg/m^3)
0	288	101.3	1.225
100	288	100.1	1.213
200	287	98.9	1.202
300	286	97.8	1.190
400	286	96.6	1.179
500	285	95.5	1.167
600	284	94.3	1.156
700	284	93.2	1.145
800	283	92.1	1.134
900	282	91.0	1.123
1,000	282	89.9	1.112
1,500	278	84.6	1.058
2,000	275	79.5	1.007
2,500	272	74.7	0.957
3,000	269	70.1	0.909
3,500	265	65.8	0.863
4,000	262	61.7	0.819
4,500	259	57.8	0.777
5,000	256	54.0	0.736
5,500	252	50.5	0.697
6,000	249	47.2	0.660
6,500	246	44.1	0.624
7,000	243	41.1	0.590
7,500	239	38.3	0.557
8,000	236	35.7	0.526
8,500	233	33.2	0.496
9,000	230	30.8	0.467
9,500	227	28.6	0.439
10,000	223	26.5	0.414
12,000	217	19.4	0.312
14,000	217	14.2	0.228
16,000	217	10.4	0.166
18,000	217	7.57	0.122
20,000	217	5.53	0.0889
22,000	217	4.04	0.0650

Figure 4-2.

EXAMPLE 4-B.

The airline flying the Boeing 747 described above stipulates that a cabin altitude of 8,000 ft. is to be maintained at all times. This is done for the comfort of the passengers and crew. Therefore the pressure in the cabin will be maintained at 1,572 lbs./ft.^{2} or 10.9 lbs./in.^{2} As, we have said the pressurization system of the Boeing 747 maintains a pressure differential is 8.9 lbs./in.^{2} Therefore, the minimum the outside air pressure can be is 10.9 – 8.9 = 2.0 lbs./in.^{2} Converting to lb./ft.^{2} gives an outside pressure of 288 lbs./ft.^{2} Referring back to the Standard Atmosphere Table, we get a maximum altitude of about 47,000 ft. The cruise ceiling for the 747 is listed as 45,000 ft.

Absolute and Relative Humidity

Since the surface of a body of water (ocean, river, lake, etc.) is exposed to the atmosphere, some water (H_2O) molecules are constantly in the process of gaining enough heat energy to escape from the water surface and enter the atmosphere. The rate of this process, evaporation, is determined by the temperature of the water. As the water molecules enter the atmosphere, they contribute a pressure of their own. The water molecules seem to ignore the presence of the air.

If the air is **saturated**, it contains as many water molecules as it can at the given temperature. The air may not be saturated and the water vapor pressure may be less than its maximum value at that temperature.

SATURATED VAPOR PRESSURE OF WATER		
TEMPERATURE ($^\circ$F)	PRESSURE (mm of Hg)	(LBS./IN.^{2})
– 40	0.097	0.0019
– 4	0.776	0.0150
14	1.95	0.0377
32	4.58	0.0886
50	9.21	0.178
68	17.53	0.339
77	23.76	0.459
86	31.82	0.615
122	92.52	1.789

Figure 4-3.

Figure 4-3 gives the saturated vapor pressure of water at various temperatures.

Absolute Humidity

The absolute humidity is the actual mass of water vapor in a given volume containing air and water, calculated from $\rho = P/RT$.

Relative Humidity

Usually, we rate humidity by using the concept of relative humidity and expressing it as a percent. The definition is:

$$\text{Relative Humidity} = \frac{\text{partial water vapor pressure}}{\text{saturated water vapor pressure}} \times 100$$

EXAMPLE 4-C.

On a given day when the temperature is 77°F, the water vapor pressure is 15.4 mmHg. By referring to figure 4-3, we see that at 77°F the saturated water vapor pressure is 23.76 mmHg. This means that the air is not holding as many water vapor molecules as it can at this temperature. The calculation of relative humidity, often just called humidity, is as follows:

$$\text{Relative Humidity} = \frac{15.4 \text{ mm Hg}}{23.76 \text{ mm Hg}} \times 100 = 65\%$$

For comfort the relative humidity should be from 40 to 50%. We see that the above situation would result in a "sticky" day.

Humidity and Comfort

When the relative humidity is high, the evaporation of moisture from the skin is slowed down. This evaporation process is the body's attempt to regulate its temperature. This is why the human body is so uncomfortable when the relative humidity is high.

As air cools, the water vapor pressure remains the same. If, on the day discussed above, when the water vapor pressure was 15.4 mmHg, the temperature goes down to 68°F, the relative humidity changes. The calculation is, for this new temperature:

$$\text{Relative Humidity} = \frac{15.4 \text{ mm Hg}}{17.53 \text{ mm Hg}} \times 100 = 88\%$$

The day which was somewhat "sticky" has now become really unbearable!

EXAMPLE 4-D.

The wintertime also has its problems with humidity. Suppose that the outside temperature is 14°F and the water vapor pressure is 0.997 mmHg. At this temperature, the saturated water vapor pressure is 1.95 mmHg.

$$\text{Relative Humidity} = \frac{0.997 \text{ mmHg}}{1.95 \text{ mmHg}} \times 100 = 51\%$$

As this air enters a non-airconditioned home heated to 68°F, the water vapor pressure remains the same. Indoors, the relative humidity can again be calculated using the fact that the saturated water vapor pressure at 68°F is 17.53 mmHg.

$$\text{Relative Humidity} = \frac{0.997 \text{ mmHg}}{17.53 \text{ mmHg}} \times 100 = 5.7\%$$

Because the relative humidity is so low inside the house (as low as the desert), perspiration evaporates very rapidly from the skin and the occupants feel very cold. In addition, such low humidity tends to aggravate the mucous membranes of the nose and throat.

Air conditioning units, if they are to work to make humans comfortable, have to adjust both the temperature and the relative humidity.

The Dew Point

The dew point is the temperature at which the air, having a definite water vapor pressure, becomes saturated. For example, from the table we see that at 77°F the saturated water vapor pressure is 23.76 mmHg. If the temperature is above 77°F and the water vapor pressure is 23.76 mmHg the relative humidity is less than 100%. However, if the temperature cools to the dew point (77°F for this water vapor pressure) the relative humidity becomes 100% and condensation occurs on all surfaces.

Avogadro's Law

In order to explain the observed behavior of gases which react chemically, (an example of this would be the combustion of fuel in an engine.) Amadeo Avogadro put forward (1811) the idea that "equal volumes of all gases at the same temperature and pressure contain the same number of molecules". This idea has since been proven theoretically and experimentally and is now referred to as Avogardo's law.

Suppose we have two containers which have the same volume. And suppose that one of the containers is filled with a certain gas which might be a mixture like air or a pure substance like oxygen. The other container also contains some gas, hydrogen, acetylene, petroleum vapor, etc. What Avogadro's law tells us is that if both the temperature and pressure in the two containers is the same then "counting" the number of molecules in each container would give the same answer.

Consider a volume of dry air (no water molecules). And to be very clear suppose it contains exactly 100 molecules, 20 oxygen and 80 nitrogen. The average mass of these molecules measured in atomic mass units is 29 so that the total mass of the air in our volume would be 2,900 amu. Now consider an equal volume of air with water vapor present so that in addition to the oxygen and nitrogen molecules, water molecules are present. If the temperature and pressure in the two volumes of air are the same, then by Avogadro's law, the volume with the water molecules must also contain 100 molecules. If, for example, our volume contains 5 water molecules then the total of nitrogen and oxygen molecules will be 95.

This allows us to understand two important effects which water vapor has on the performance of aircraft. First, the lift on an aircraft depends directly on the density (mass per unit volume) of the air streaming past the surfaces of the craft. The average mass of a molecule of dry air (oxygen and nitrogen) is 29 atomic mass units, while the mass of a water molecule is only 18 atomic mass units. With water vapor in the air, molecules with an average mass of 29 amu have been replaced by molecules with a mass of 18 amu thus decreasing the density and reducing the lift on the aircraft.

The second effect has to do with the combustion process in the powerplant of the aircraft. As we have seen, a given volume of air with water vapor present has less oxygen in it than an equal volume of dry air other conditions being the same (water has replaced the oxygen). Since oxygen is the component of the air responsible for combustion, if the fuel air mixture provided by the carburetor is set for dry air conditions and there is water vapor present in the air there will be inadequate oxygen. This will result in incomplete combustion, and a loss of power.

Chapter IV Problems

1. Verify. that using the Gas Law (ρ = P/RT) and the temperature and pressure from the Standard Atmosphere Table, at an altitude of 65,000 ft., the density of air is 0.000178 slug/ft.^{3}

2. A pressurized Cessna Centurion II has a cabin pressurization system which can maintain a pressure differential of 3.45 lbs./in.^{2} What is the maximum altitude at which the plane can fly and still maintain a cabin altitude of 8,000 feet?

3. What is the maximum altitude at which this same Cessna plane can fly and maintain a cabin altitude of 6,000 ft.?

4. On a day when the temperature is 86 °F the water vapor pressure is 21.2 mmHg.
   (a) What is the relative humidity?
   (b) The temperature changes suddenly to 77 °F while the water vapor pressure remains the same. What is the new relative humidity?

5. On a day when the temperature is 14°F the water vapor pressure is 1.23 mmHg.
   (a) What is the relative humidity?
   (b) As this air enters a house heated to 77 °F, what is the relative humidity inside the house?

6. On a day when the outside temperature is 50 °F and the vapor pressure is 8.86 mmHg, what is the relative humidity? What is the relative humidity in the cabin of a 747 where the temperature is 68 °F and the vapor pressure is the same as the outside air? Will the passengers be comfortable?

Chapter V

Motion and Acceleration

Definition

When a body is moving in a straight line with constant speed it is **not** accelerating. We say, in this case, that it is moving with constant velocity. If a body's velocity is not constant, it is accelerating. A body accelerates if it is changing its speed and/or its direction.

When we discuss a body's straight-line motion, then we do not have any change in direction. In this special case, any acceleration is due to a change in speed.

Special Formulas Dealing with Straight-Line Motion

In all of the following discussion, certain symbols will be used. These symbols are summarized below:

$$v_{av} = \text{average velocity}$$
$$t = \text{time}$$
$$v_i = \text{initial velocity}$$
$$v_f = \text{final velocity}$$
$$a = \text{acceleration}$$
$$* \quad s = \text{distance covered}$$

* Note that s is the traditional notation for distance in almost all physics textbooks. This choice reduces confusion with the symbol d, for derivative, a concept from calculus.

There is a formula dealing with the motion of a body that you have used for many years. In grade school, you probably memorized the formula in these words:

$$\text{distance} = \text{rate} \times \text{time}$$

Using our above symbols, we could write:

$$(1) \qquad s = v_{av}t$$

Note that for the rate, we have used the average speed. We all know that even though sometimes speed changes, we can always talk about the average speed. Thus, if we travel at an average speed of 50 MPH for 6 hours, we cover 300 miles.

Now we must extend our treatment of motion to include the concept of acceleration. Acceleration (for straight-line motion) is the rate of change of speed in time. We define acceleration (for straight-line motion) in the following manner:

$$(2) \qquad a = \frac{v_f - v_i}{t}$$

In using this formula, a may be either positive or negative. If v_f is less than v_i, then our value of a turns out to be a negative number.

EXAMPLE 5-A.

A truck is initially travelling at a speed of 50 ft./sec. The driver applies his brakes for 15 sec. The final speed of the car is 20 ft./sec. What is the acceleration?

$$a = \frac{20 \text{ ft./sec.} - 50 \text{ ft./sec.}}{15 \text{ sec.}}$$

$$a = \frac{-30 \text{ ft./sec.}}{15 \text{ sec.}}$$

$$a = -2 \frac{\text{ft./sec.}}{\text{sec.}} = -2 \frac{\text{ft.}}{\text{sec.}} \frac{1}{\text{sec.}}$$

$$a = -2 \frac{\text{ft.}}{\text{sec.}^2}$$

Notice that the unit of acceleration has the square of a time unit in its denominator.

A little thought will convince you that an acceleration is positive if the body is increasing speed and negative when the body is decreasing its speed.

If we cross-multiply in formula (2) we obtain:

$$at = v_f - v_i$$

After transposing, we can write:

$$(3) \qquad v_f = v_i + at$$

If an automobile is on an expressway and the driver is increasing speed smoothly and regularly, we note that his average speed is the average of his initial and final speed.

The equation can be written:

$$v_{av} = \frac{v_f + v_i}{2}$$

If this value of v_{av} is substituted into equation (1), we have:

(4)
$$s = \frac{v_f + v_i}{2} t$$

In this equation, we can substitute for v_f using the value in equation (3).

(5)
$$s = \frac{v_i + at + v_i}{2} t = \frac{2v_i + at}{2} t$$

After a bit of algebra, we obtain:

(6)
$$s = v_i t + \frac{1}{2} at_2$$

Equation (4) can be written, after cross-multiplication:

(7)
$$2s = (v_f + v_i) t$$

We can now multiply equation (2) by equation (7). After cancelling time (t) on the right:

$$2as = (v_f - v_i)(v_f + v_i)$$

or
$$2as = v_f^2 - v_i^2$$

The final form of this formula is:

(8)
$$v_f^2 = v_i^2 + 2as$$

Equations (4), (3), (6), and (8) are very important formulas. They enable us to deal with all kinds of motion problems where the body is in straight line motion and is changing its speed. These formulas will be summarized below. They will be numbered with Roman numerals and can be referred to by these numbers when used in the problem exercises.

I.
$$s = \frac{v_f + v_i}{2} t$$

II.
$$v_f = v_i + at$$

III.
$$s = v_i t + \frac{1}{2} at^2$$

IV.
$$v_f^2 = v_i^2 + 2as$$

When a body in straight line motion is not changing speed, or in cases where we are interested only in the average speed, the formula is more simple.

$$s = v_{av} t$$

Formulas I through IV are used in many practical physics problems. Note that each one involves four quantities. When a problem is given to you to solve, be sure to determine which of these three quantities are given to you, and which quantity is to be found. Choose the formula which involves these four quantities. If the formula is not solved for the unknown quantity, solve for this quantity algebraically. Finally substitute the known quantities and solve for the unknown quantity.

An example should clarify the above procedure.

EXAMPLE 5-B.

An automobile has an initial speed of 50 ft./sec. and a final speed of 75 ft./sec. While it is undergoing this change of speed, it travels a distance of 125 ft. What is its acceleration?

In attacking this problem it is wise to write down exactly what is known and what is unknown.

v_i = 50 ft./sec.	v_f = 75 ft./sec.
s = 125 ft.	a = ?

Formula IV involves these four quantities. Note that I, II, and III do not involve these exact four quantities. Formula IV is the one to use. First it should be solved for the unknown, a.

$$v_f^2 = v_i^2 + 2as$$

$$v_f^2 - v_i^2 = 2as$$

$$a = \frac{v_f^2 - v_i^2}{2s}$$

$$a = \frac{(75 \text{ ft./sec.})^2 - (50 \text{ ft./sec.})^2}{2(125 \text{ ft.})}$$

$$a = \frac{3125 \text{ ft.}^2/\text{sec.}^2}{250 \text{ ft.}} = 12.5 \frac{\text{ft.}^2}{\text{sec.}^2} \frac{1}{\text{ft.}}$$

$$a = 12.5 \frac{\text{ft.}}{\text{sec.}^2}$$

Accelerated Motion of a "Freely Falling" Body

Common experience indicates that falling bodies accelerate or increase in speed as they fall. Close to the surface of the earth this "acceleration of a freely falling body" has been measured to be about 32 ft./sec.^{2} in the English system and 9.8 m/sec.^{2} in the metric system. The "about" in the preceding sentence indicates that this quantity varies somewhat over the face of our earth. The values given are average values.

When we use the words "freely falling", we mean that we are neglecting the effects of air resistance (as if we were in a vacuum). Of course, there is always air resistance, so how can we neglect it?

When a body is falling with a great speed, air resistance can certainly not be neglected. To use the acceleration formulas in these cases would give us results that are not valid. However, if a body is falling close to the surface of the earth, the acceleration formulas do give us valid results if the height from which it falls is not too great.

Some numerical data should clarify the preceding statements. If a compact body, such as a stone, is dropped (not thrown) from a height of 324 ft. above the surface of the earth, it will take about 4.5 sec. for the body to reach the ground. It will have obtained a speed of 144 ft./sec. (98 MPH). At this speed, the effects of air resistance are still quite negligible. Above this speed (98 MPH), the effects of air resistance are not negligible.

Therefore, we can conclude that the fall of a body from a height of 324 ft. or less (or equivalently during a time of 4.5 sec. or less) can be handled quite accurately with the ordinary acceleration formulas. The value of the acceleration will be either

9.8 m/sec.^{2} or 32 ft./sec.^{2} If the body is rising and therefore decreasing its speed the values of the acceleration will be –9.8 m/sec.^{2} or –32 ft./sec.^{2}

If a body falls from a height greater than about 324 ft. above the surface of the earth, the air resistance becomes very important. As we have said, a height of 324 ft. corresponds to a fall of 4.5 sec. When the time of fall increases to about 8 seconds, the speed of fall has increased to about 115 MPH. When the time of fall is between 4.5 sec. and 8 sec. the speed increases in a nonlinear manner from 98 MPH to 115 MPH. As the time of fall increases beyond 8 seconds the speed of fall remains constant at about 115 MPH. This speed of fall is called the "terminal velocity".

All of the above data indicates that it is possible to use the acceleration formulas with accurate results for many applications dealing with falling bodies. We will limit our applications to cases where the formulas are valid: heights less than 324 ft. and times of fall less than 4.5 seconds.

EXAMPLE 5-C.

A body started from rest and has been falling freely for 3 sec. At what speed is it falling?

$$v_i = 0$$

$$t = 3 \text{ sec}$$

$$a = 32 \text{ ft./sec.}^2$$

We will use Formula II.

$$v_f = v_i + at$$

$$v_f = 0 + \left(32 \frac{\text{ft.}}{\text{sec.}^2}\right)(3 \text{ sec.})$$

$$v_f = 96 \frac{\text{ft.}}{\text{sec.}}$$

EXAMPLE 5-D.

A body started at rest and has been falling freely for 3 sec. How far has it fallen?

$$v_i = 0$$

$$t = 3 \text{ sec}$$

$$a = 32 \text{ ft./sec.}^2$$

$$s = ?$$

We will use Formula III.

$$s = v_i t + \frac{1}{2}at^2$$

$$s = (0)(3 \text{ sec.}) + \frac{1}{2}(32 \frac{\text{ft.}}{\text{sec.}^2})(3 \text{ sec.})^2$$

$$s = 144 \text{ ft.}$$

EXAMPLE 5-E.

A body is thrown upward with an initial speed of 120 ft./sec. How high does it rise?

$$v_i = 120 \text{ ft./sec.}$$

$$v_f = 0$$

$$a = -32 \text{ ft./sec.}^2$$

$$s = ?$$

We will use Formula IV.

$$v_f{}^2 = v_i{}^2 + 2as$$

$$s = \frac{v_f{}^2 - v_i{}^2}{2a}$$

$$s = \frac{0 - (120 \frac{\text{ft.}}{\text{sec.}})^2}{2(-32 \text{ ft./sec.}^2)}$$

$$s = 225 \frac{\text{ft.}^2}{\text{sec.}^2} \cdot \frac{\text{sec.}^2}{\text{ft.}}$$

$$s = 225 \text{ ft.}$$

Centripetal Acceleration

There is another type of acceleration called centripetal (centerseeking) acceleration. It occurs when a body is moving with constant speed in a circular path. Such a motion occurs when a plane moves in a circular path or loop.

In this kind of motion, the body is accelerating, not because it is changing its speed, but because it is changing its direction. When we deal with the causes of acceleration (forces), you will understand how important it is to understand centripetal acceleration. We need to know what must be done to keep a body moving in a circular path. A body must be pulled to the center of a circular path. If this center-directed pull is not present, the body will move off along a tangent. We note that:

$$\Delta = \text{"change in"}$$

Refer to figure 5-1. The speed of the body is not changing, therefore, the lengths of the vectors v_1 and v_2 are the same.

$$v_1 = v_2 = v$$

Also, Δv is the change in the velocity vector. Arc s approximately equals chord s.

The triangles are similar (same shape) and, therefore, the sides are proportional.

$$\frac{s}{R} = \frac{\Delta v}{v}$$

$$\Delta v = \frac{sv}{R}$$

Divide each side of this equation by t.

$$\frac{\Delta v}{t} = \frac{s\,v}{t\,R}$$

We recall that the velocity equals the distance (s) divided by the time (t).

$$\frac{\Delta v}{t} = v\frac{v}{R}$$

We also recall that acceleration equals the **change in velocity** divided by the time in which this change occurs.

$$\text{Centripetal Acceleration} = a_c = \frac{v^2}{R}$$

This formula says that the centripetal acceleration equals the square of the speed divided by the radius of the circular path.

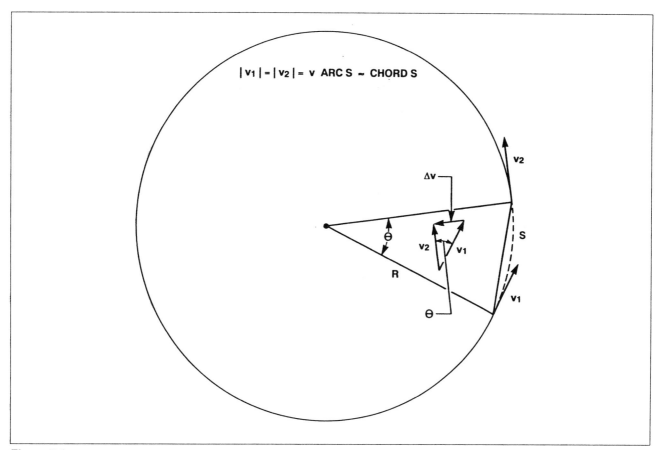

Figure 5-1.

Chapter V Problems

1. An automobile on an expressway is accelerating at 25 ft./sec.^{2} If it started from rest and has been accelerating for 4.56 sec., how far has it traveled during this time of acceleration?

2. A truck had an initial velocity of 40 ft./sec. It accelerated at 10 ft./sec.^{2} and reached a final velocity of 65 ft./sec. How far did this truck travel while it was accelerating?

3. A car slowed down from 75 ft./sec. to 40 ft./sec. while traveling a distance of 125 ft. What was its acceleration?

4. A car, originally traveling at 25 ft./sec., increases its speed at a rate of 5 ft./sec.^{2} for a period of 6 sec. What was its final speed?

5. A truck, originally traveling at 78 ft./sec., slows down to 34 ft./sec. during a 7 sec. interval. What is its acceleration?

6. A car has an initial velocity of 45 ft./sec. It slows down at a rate of 5 ft./sec.^{2} and covers a distance of 56 ft. while slowing down. What is its final velocity?

7. A stone is dropped from a high building and falls freely for 3.5 sec. How far (in meters) has it fallen during this time?

8. A stone is thrown upward with an initial velocity of 125 ft./sec. How high does it rise?

9. A baseball is thrown upward with an initial velocity of 125 ft./sec. What is the time of rise?

10. A ball is dropped from a bridge into the river below and 2.5 sec. after the ball is dropped a splash is heard in the water below. How high is the bridge?

11. A car starts with an initial velocity of 34 ft./sec. and accelerates for 5.6 sec. at 4 ft./sec.^{2} How far has it traveled during this time?

12. A car starts at an initial velocity of 55 ft./sec. and comes to rest in 6 sec. How far has it traveled during this time?

13. A Piper Arrow has a take-off run of 1,110 feet, at the end of which its speed is 69.6 knots. What is the acceleration of the plane during the run?

14. A Cessna Agcarryall has a take-off run of 885 feet, at the end of which its speed is 78 MPH. How much time does the run take?

15. A Grumman Tomcat, powered by two Pratt & Whitney turbofan engines, has a maximum acceleration during take-off of 23 ft./sec.^{2} What velocity can it achieve by the end of a 900 foot take-off run?

16. A plane is executing a horizontal turn at a speed of 255 MPH. The radius of the turn is 1,000 ft. What is the centripetal acceleration in ft./sec.^{2}?

17. A boy is swinging a stone at the end of a string. The stone is moving in a circular path. The speed of the stone is 5 ft./sec. and the radius of the path is 1.5 ft. What is the centripetal acceleration of the stone?

Chapter VI

Newton's Laws

The rapid advance in aviation in the first half of this century can be attributed in large part to a science of motion which was presented to the world three centuries ago by Sir Isaac Newton, a British physicist. Published in 1686, Newton's treatise on motion, **The Principia**, showed how all observed motions could be explained on the basis of three laws. The applications of these laws have led to great technological advances in the aerodynamics, structure, and power plant of aircraft. It is safe to say that any future improvements in the performance of aircraft will be based on these laws. This chapter will be devoted to Newton's laws, examining some of their applications in aviation.

Newton's First Law

The old magician's trick of pulling a cloth out from under a full table setting is not only a reflection of the magician's skill but also an affirmation of a natural tendency which dishes and silverware share with all matter. This natural tendency for objects at rest to remain at rest can be attested to by any child who ever tried kicking a large rock out of his path. It is also a well known fact that once a gun is fired, the command "stop" has no effect on the bullet. Only the intervention of some object can stop or deflect it from its course. This characteristic of matter to persist in its state of rest or continue in whatever state of motion it happens to be in is called inertia. This property is the basis of a principle of motion which was first enunciated by Galileo in the early part of the 17th century and later adopted by Newton as his first law of motion.

The first law of motion is called the law of inertia. It can be summarized:

A body at rest remains at rest and a body in motion continues to move at constant velocity unless acted upon by an unbalanced external force.

The importance of the law of inertia is that it tells us what to expect in the absence of forces, either rest (no motion) or straight line motion at constant speed. A passenger's uncomfortable experience of being thrown forward when an airplane comes to a sudden stop at the terminal is an example of this principle in action. A more violent example is the collision of a vehicle with a stationary object. The vehicle is often brought to an abrupt stop.

Unconstrained passengers continue to move with the velocity they had just prior to the collision only to be brought to rest (all too frequently with tragic consequences) by surfaces within the vehicle (dashboards, windshields, etc.).

A less dramatic example of Newton's first law comes from the invigorating activity of shoveling snow. Scooping up a shovel full of snow, a person swings the shovel and then brings it to a sudden stop. The snow having acquired the velocity of the shovel continues its motion leaving the shovel and going off onto the snow pile.

Newton's Second Law

A Learjet accelerates down the runway a distance of 3,000 feet, takes off and begins its climb at 6,000 feet per minute quickly reaching a cruising altitude of 35,000 feet, where it levels off at a speed of 260 knots. Subsequently, the plane may have to perform a variety of maneuvers involving changes in heading, elevation, and speed. Every aspect of the airplane's motion is governed by the external forces acting on its wings, fuselage, control surfaces and power plant. The skilled pilot using his controls continually adjusts these forces to make the plane perform as desired.

The interplay between force and motion is the subject of Newton's second law. An understanding of this law not only provides insight into the flight of a plane, but allows us to analyze the motion of any object.

While Newton's first law tells us that uniform velocity is to be expected when an object moves in the absence of external forces, the second law states that to have a change in speed or direction an unbalanced force must act on the object. Using acceleration to describe the change in motion of an object, the second law can be expressed:

$$F_{net} = ma$$

In words, the second law states that a net or unbalanced force acting on an object equals the mass of the object times the acceleration of that object.

Here, the net force is the total force acting on the object, obtained by adding vectorially all of the forces influencing the object. The mass is a scalar quantity. However, both the net force and the acceleration are vector quantities. Mathematically, this means that they must always point in the same direction. That is, at each instant the acceleration is in the same direction as the net force.

Before we consider cases where the net force acting on a body is not zero, it is most important to understand that sometimes the net force acting on a body is zero. The vector sum of the forces acting on the body in the x-direction is zero and the vector sum of the forces acting on the body in the y-direction is also zero. In this case we say that the body is in equilibrium. From the law, net force equals mass times acceleration, we know that since the net force is zero the acceleration is also zero. Zero acceleration means that the velocity of the body in not changing in direction or in magnitude. This means that the body is moving in a straight line with constant speed or it has the constant speed, zero (it is at rest). If we observe that a body is at rest we know that all of the forces on this body are balanced. Similarly, if a body is moving in a straight line with constant speed, all of the forces acting on this body are balanced.

For example, if a plane is traveling on a straight stretch of runway at constant speed, there are four forces acting on this plane: the earth is pulling down on the plane (its weight), the earth is pushing up on the plane (the normal force), the engine is giving a forward thrust to the plane, and frictional forces (air resistance, tires on runway, etc.) are acting backward. This is illustrated in figure 6-1.

Next, we must consider some examples where the net force acting on a body is not zero. The body is accelerating. The body is experiencing a change in its direction or in its speed or both. As a first example, a plane accelerating down a runway gets a change in velocity in the direction of its motion. This is the same direction as the thrust provided by the power plant.

In figure 6-2, note that the thrust is greater than the frictional forces. The net forward force is the

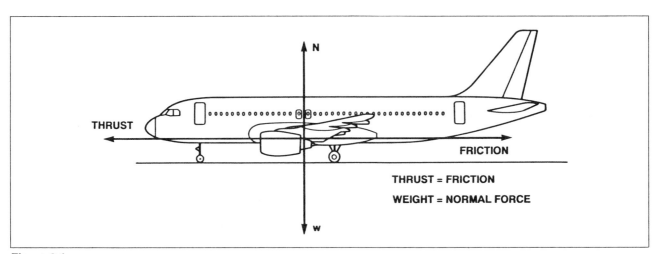

Figure 6-1.

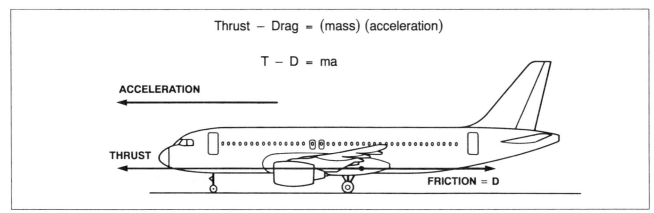

Figure 6-2.

38

thrust minus the friction. It is this net forward force that results in the acceleration of the plane.

In the last chapter, it was demonstrated that a ball whirled in a circle experiences an acceleration toward the center of the circle. This acceleration is in the same direction as the force of tension in the string which tethers the ball to the center of its revolution.

In figure 6-3, we have a constant change in the direction of the motion of the ball. Therefore, we have a constant acceleration. We recall that the centripetal acceleration was calculated to be the square of the velocity divided by the radius of the circular path. Thus, we can write the equation:

$$F_{net} = ma_c \qquad \text{or} \qquad F_{net} = \frac{mv^2}{R}$$

The units which we will use in our discussion of Newton's laws are the same as the units used in the formula relating weight to mass (w = mg). These units are reviewed and summarized in figure 6-4.

Each set of units (pound, slug, ft./sec.^{2}) in the English system, or (newton, kilogram, m/sec.^{2}) in the metric system is said to be consistent in the following sense. A force of 1 lb. when applied to a mass of 1 slug gives it an acceleration of 1 ft./sec.^{2}.

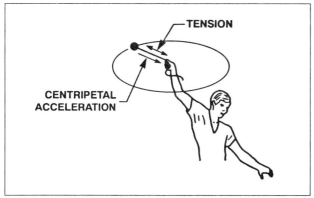

Figure 6-3.

UNITS	ENGLISH	METRIC
Force	pound (lb.)	newton (N)
Mass	slug	kilogram (kg)
Acceleration	ft./sec.^{2}	m/sec.^{2}

Figure 6-4.

Similarly, a force of 1 newton applied to a mass of 1 kilogram causes it to accelerate at 1 m/sec.^{2}.

Using Newton's second law, we can write:

$$1 \text{ newton} = 1 \text{ kilogram m/sec.}^2$$
$$\text{and} \qquad 1 \text{ pound} = 1 \text{ slug ft./sec.}^2$$

We note that Newton's second law is correctly written as:

$$F_{net} = ma$$

However, we often assume that the force acting on mass (m) is the net force. Thus, we usually write the second law simply as:

$$F = ma$$

or, for circular motion,

$$F = \frac{mv^2}{R} \quad \text{(Centripetal Force)}$$

Newton's second law when applied to bodies moving in a circular path states that the force directed toward the center of the path must equal the mass of the body times the square of the speed of the body divided by the radius of the path. This force is called the centripetal (center-directed) force.

EXAMPLE 6-A.

Find the acceleration of a 3 slug object acted upon by a net force of 1.5 lbs.

$$a = \frac{F}{m}$$

$$a = \frac{1.5 \text{ lbs.}}{3 \text{ slugs}}$$

$$a = 0.5 \text{ ft./sec.}^2$$

EXAMPLE 6-B.

A mass of 6 kilograms accelerates at 5 m/sec.^{2} Find the force which is acting on this object.

$$F = ma$$

$$F = (6 \text{ kg})(5 \text{ m/sec.}^2) = 30 \text{ N}$$

Newton's Third Law

Newton's third law is sometimes referred to as the law of action and reaction. This law focuses on the fact that forces, the pushes and pulls responsible for both the stability of structures as well as the acceleration of an object, arise from the interaction of two objects. A push, for example, must involve two objects, the object being pushed and the object doing the pushing.

The third law states that no matter what the circumstance, when one object exerts a force an a second object the second must exert an exactly equal and oppositely directed force on the first. An apple hanging from a tree is pulled by the earth with a force which we call its weight. Newton's third law tells us that the apple must pull back on the earth with an exactly equal force. The weight of the apple is a force on the apple by the earth, directed downward. The force which the apple exerts back on the earth, is a pull on the earth directed upward. Another force acting on the apple is the upward pull exerted by the branch. The law of action and reaction tells us that the apple must be pulling down on the branch with the same magnitude of force.

People are often confused by this principle because it implies, for instance, that in a tug of war the winning team pulls no harder than the losing team. Equally enigmatic is how a horse and wagon manage to move forward if the wagon pulls back on the horse with the same force the horse pulls forward on the wagon. We can understand the results of the tug of war by realizing that the motion of the winning team (or losing team) is not determined exclusively by the pull of the other team, but also the force which the ground generates on the team members feet when they "dig in". Recall, it is the net force, the sum of all of the acting forces which determines the motion of an object.

The results of a "tug of war" can be quite different if the "winning team", no matter how big and strong, is standing on ice while the "losing team" is able to establish good solid footing on rough terrain.

Similarly, the horse moves forward because the reaction force which the ground exerts in the forward direction on its hooves is greater than the backward pull it receives from the wagon. By focusing now on the wagon, we see that it moves forward because the forward pull of the horse is greater than the

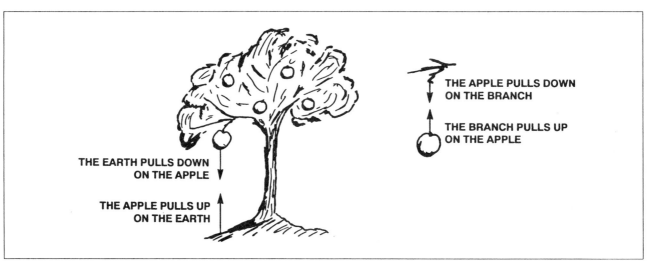

THE APPLE PULLS DOWN ON THE BRANCH

THE BRANCH PULLS UP ON THE APPLE

THE EARTH PULLS DOWN ON THE APPLE

THE APPLE PULLS UP ON THE EARTH

Figure 6-5.

Figure 6-6.

backward pull of friction between its wheels and the ground.

One of the main difficulty people have with the third law comes from not realizing that the action and reaction forces act on different objects and therefore can never cancel. Another difficulty comes from forgetting that the motion of an object is determined by the sum of all of the forces acting on that object.

In canoeing or rowing, a paddle is used to push water backward. The water reacts back on the paddle generating a forward force which propels the boat.

Consider now a propeller as shown in figure 6-8.

The plane of rotation of the propeller is assumed to be perpendicular to the plane of the paper. The flow of air is from left to right. We can imagine the action of the propeller is to take a mass (M) of air on the left and accelerate it from some initial velocity (v_i) to a final velocity (v_f) to the right of the propeller. The acceleration of this air mass requires a force which is provided by the propeller. The air mass, in turn, reacts with an equal and opposite force on the propeller. This reaction force of the air on the propeller provides the thrust for a propeller driven plane. The acceleration of the air mass is:

$$a = \frac{v_f - v_i}{t}$$

Substituting this into Newton's second law, we find for the net force on the air mass:

$$F = M\frac{v_f - v_i}{t}$$

Both of the velocities (v_i and v_f) are the velocities relative to the plane of rotation of the propeller. The time (t) is the time involved in accelerating the air mass from v_i to v_f.

By Newton's third law, the thrust, which is the force the air mass exerts back on the propeller, is equal in magnitude to F. Therefore, the thrust (T) is given by:

$$T = M\frac{v_f - v_i}{t}$$

Recall that we have a symbol for "change in", this means that we can write the above formula as:

$$T = M\frac{\Delta v}{t}$$

The velocities of the air mass are relative to the plane, and therefore change as the plane's speed changes. Also the time involved in accelerating the air mass changes with the speed of the plane. This causes considerable variation in the thrust provided by a propeller.

FORCE OF PADDLE ON WATER　　　**FORCE OF WATER ON PADDLE**

Figure 6-7.

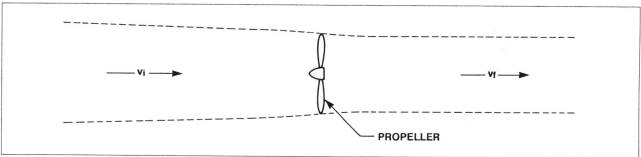

v_i　　　v_f

— PROPELLER

Figure 6-8.

EXAMPLE 6-C.

Each second a propeller accelerates an air mass of 12.2 slugs from rest to a velocity of 137 ft./sec. How much thrust is provided?

$$T = (12.2 \text{ slugs}) \frac{137 \text{ ft./sec.} - 0}{1 \text{ sec.}}$$

$$T = 1,670 \text{ lbs.}$$

In contrast to the reciprocating engine driven propeller which imparts a small change in velocity to a relatively large mass of air, a turbojet induces a large change in velocity to a relatively small mass of air. Here, the sole action of the jet engine is considered to be the intake of a mass of air at some velocity (vi) and its exhaust at a higher velocity (vf).

Figure 6-9 is a sketch of a turbojet engine. The velocity (vi) in the figure denotes the relative intake velocity and v_f denotes the exhaust gas velocity. The thrust formula which was obtained above for the propeller will now be applied to a jet engine. The thrust formula above can be rewritten:

$$T = \frac{M}{t} v_f - \frac{M}{t} v_i$$

$$T = \text{Gross Thrust} - \text{Ram Drag}$$

The gross thrust is provided by the exhaust gases. The ram drag of the incoming air is due to the speed of the airplane. The effect of the ram drag is to reduce the thrust provided by the engine as the speed of the plane increases.

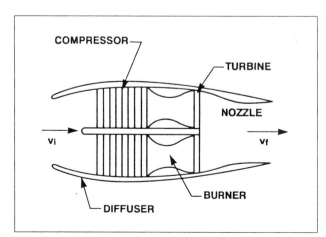

Figure 6-9.

EXAMPLE 6-D.

The Pratt & Whitney J60 has a mass air flow of 23 kg/sec. During a static test (initial velocity = 0) the exhaust velocity was measured to be 580 m/sec. Determine the thrust produced.

Note that the ram drag is zero since v_i is zero.

Therefore, the thrust is equal simply to the gross thrust.

$$T = \frac{M}{t} v_f$$

Substituting the given values we have:

$$T = \frac{23 \text{ kg}}{1 \text{ sec.}} (580 \text{ m/sec.})$$

$$T = 13,300 \text{ N}$$

EXAMPLE 6-E.

What would the thrust have been if the J60 of the previous example had been in a plane moving at 250 knots? Assume the same mass flow and exhaust velocity.

Note that the ram drag is not zero in this case. In order to calculate this ram drag we must use the formula:

$$\text{ram drag} = \frac{M}{t} v_i$$

Before substituting, we must express the initial velocity in m/sec.

$$v_i = 250 \text{ knots} \times \frac{1.668 \text{ ft./sec.}}{1 \text{ knot}} \times \frac{0.30480 \text{ m}}{1 \text{ ft.}}$$
$$= 129 \text{ m/sec.}$$

$$\text{ram drag} = \frac{23 \text{ kg}}{1 \text{ sec.}} 129 \text{ m/sec.}$$

$$\text{ram drag} = 2,970 \text{ N}$$

$$T = \text{gross thrust} - \text{ram drag}$$

$$T = 13,300 \text{ N} - 2,970 \text{ N}$$

$$T = 10,300 \text{ N}$$

EXAMPLE 6-F.

During a static test (initial velocity = zero), a Pratt & Whitney J75 produced a thrust of 16,000 lbs. with an air mass flow of 8.23 slugs/sec. Determine the exhaust gas velocity of the engine.

Since v_i is zero, the ram drag is zero and T = gross thrust.

$$T = \frac{M}{t} v_f$$

We solve for the final velocity:

$$v_f = \frac{T}{M/t}$$

$$v_f = \frac{16,000 \text{ lbs.}}{8.23 \text{ slugs/sec.}}$$

$$v_f = 1,940 \text{ ft./sec.}$$

The air intake velocity of a turbojet will be approximately equal to the airspeed of the plane. Let us again examine the thrust formula.

$$T = \frac{M}{t} (v_f - v_i)$$

It can be seen that the thrust may be increased in two ways, either by increasing the air mass flow through the engine (M/t) or increasing the exhaust gas velocity (v_f).

EXAMPLE 6-G.

A French Dassault Falcon 30 is powered by two Lycoming ALF 502 turbofan engines. Flying at sea level with a velocity of 154 m/sec. the air intake velocity is 154 m/sec. and the air exhaust velocity is 224 m/sec. The airflow through each engine is 109 kg per second. Determine the thrust of each engine.

$$T = \frac{109 \text{ kg}}{1 \text{ sec.}} (224 \text{ m/sec.} - 154 \text{ m/sec.})$$

$$T = 7,630 \text{ N}$$

EXAMPLE 6-H.

A Lockheed Jet Star is equipped with four Pratt & Whitney JT12 engines. Cruising at 220 knots, each engine was found to be providing 1,420 lbs. of thrust. If the airflow through each engine was 1.55 slug/sec., what was the exhaust gas velocity?

$$v_i = 220 \text{ knots} = 371 \text{ ft./sec.}$$

$$\frac{T t}{M} = v_f - v_i$$

$$v_f = \frac{T t}{M} + v_i$$

$$v_f = \frac{(1,420 \text{ lbs.}) (1 \text{ sec.})}{1.55 \text{ slug}} + 371 \text{ ft./sec.}$$

$$v_f = 1,290 \text{ ft./sec.}$$

Chapter VI Problems

1. Find the mass of an object which accelerates at 5 m/sec.^{2} when acted on by a net force of one newton.

2. Find the acceleration of a 3 slug object experiencing a net force of 12 lbs.

3. Find the net force on a 5 slug object which is accelerating at 3 ft./sec.^{2}

4. What centripetal force is needed to keep a 3 slug ball moving in a circular path of radius 2 feet and speed 4 ft./sec.?

5. A plane weighs 36,000 lbs. The forward thrust on the plane is 20,000 lbs. and the frictional forces (drag) add up to 2,000 lbs. What is the acceleration of this plane? Hint: Be sure to find the mass of the plane from its weight.

6. The four engines of a Boeing 747-100 transport can produce a combined thrust of 176,000 lbs. at takeoff. The plane begins its roll with an acceleration of 7.56 ft./sec.^{2} Frictional forces are negligible. What is the mass of the transport at this instant? What is the weight of the transport at this instant?

7. A Learjet Model 24 of mass 5,910 kg is observed to accelerate at the start of its takeoff at 4.3 m/sec.^{2} What is the net forward force acting on the plane at this time?

8. At one moment during the takeoff of a Jetstar, its acceleration was found to be 8.95 ft./sec.^{2}, while the thrust of its engines was 12,000 lbs. Due to fuel burnoff the weight of the plane at this moment was determined to be 41,100 lbs. What was the drag (backward frictional force) on the Jetstar at this instant?

9. During a static test, a Continental engine driving a two blade constant speed propeller was found to accelerate each second a mass of 142 kg from rest to a velocity of 40 m/sec. Determine the thrust on the propeller.

10. At the beginning of its take-off, each of the two turboprop engines of a Beechcraft Super King was generating a thrust of 13,500 N. If the change in velocity of the air from fore to aft of the propeller was 52.5 m/sec., what was the mass of air being accelerated through each engine each second?

11. A Cessna Centurion II equipped with a 300 horsepower engine driving a three blade constant speed propeller can generate 1,250 lbs. of thrust while each second accelerating 9.5 slugs of air through the plane of rotation of the propeller. What is the change in velocity of the air induced by the propeller?

12. A Cessna Corsair is powered by two turboprop engines. If each engine can produce a thrust of 2,400 lbs. while changing the velocity of the air from fore to aft of the propeller by 143 ft./sec., what mass of air passes through the plane of rotation of the propeller each second?

13. A Piper Archer II has an Avco Lycoming engine driving a two blade propeller. Each second 8 slugs of air are given a change in velocity of 122 ft./sec. How much thrust is generated on the propeller?

14. A Learjet Model 24B is powered by two General Electric CJ 6106 turbojet engines. The static thrust was determined to be 2,950 lbs. with a total airflow of 1.37 slug/sec. Determine the exhaust gas velocity.

15. At a cruising speed of 481 MPH, what would be the available thrust in problem 1 if we assume that the airflow rate and exhaust gas velocity were the same as for that problem.

16. The Garrett TFE 731-3-1D turbofan engine which powers the Rockwell Saberliner 65 under static testing has an exhaust gas velocity of 321 m/sec. and an airflow of 51.2 kg/sec. Find the static thrust of the engine.

17. The Garret TFE 731-3-1D has an airflow of 42.8 kg/sec. while the Saberliner cruises at 12 200 meters (40,000 feet) at a speed of Mach 0.8 (236 m/sec.). Assuming an exhaust gas velocity of 321 m/sec., determine the thrust produced by the engine under these conditions.

18. The Pratt & Whitney JT 9D-7F used in the Boeing 747 has an airflow rate of 698 kg/sec. and an exhaust velocity of 306 m/sec. Determine the static thrust of the engine.

19. At an altitude of 10,665 m (35,000 feet) and a cruising speed of Mach 0.85 (252 m/sec.) the Pratt & Whitney JT 9D-7F in the Boeing 747 has a mass flow of 879 kg/sec. and an exhaust velocity of 306 m/sec. Find the thrust.

Chapter VII

Work, Friction, Energy, Power, and Bernoulli's Principle

Work

Work is done on a body when a force acts through a distance. The definition of work involves the force acting on the body (F) the distance through which this force acts (S) and the angle (θ) between the force vector and the distance vector. The definition of work is:

$$W = FS \cos \theta$$

Very often the force vector and the distance vector act in the same direction. In this case, the angle (θ) is a zero degree angle. If you check on your calculator, you will find that the cosine of a zero degree angle is equal to one. This simplifies things in this case because then work is simply equal to the product of force times distance.

The unit of work in the English system is the foot-lb. Note that the two units are multiplied by each other. Students tend to write ft./lb. This is **incorrect**. The unit is not feet divided by pounds. In the metric system, the unit is the Newton-meter or the Joule (J). Note that the Newton-meter has a name, the Joule. The foot-lb. has no special name.

EXAMPLE 7-A.

A puck lies on a horizontal air table. The air table reduces the friction between the puck and the table to almost zero since the puck rides on a film of air. A player exerts a force of 70 lbs. on this puck through a distance of 0.5 feet, and he is careful that his force is in the same direction as the distance through the force is applied. The player has done 35 ft.-lbs. of work on the puck.

EXAMPLE 7-B.

A book weighing 8 pounds is raised a vertical distance by a student demonstrating work. The book is raised 2 feet. The student has done 16 ft.-lbs. of work.

EXAMPLE 7-C.

A sled is dragged over a horizontal snowy surface by means of a rope attached to the front of the sled. The rope makes an angle of 28° with the horizontal. The sled is displaced a distance a 50 ft. The worker exerts a force of 35 pounds. How much work does the worker do? We use the formula:

$$W = FS \cos \theta$$

$$W = (35 \text{ lbs.}) (50 \text{ ft.}) \cos 28°$$

$$W = 1550 \text{ ft.-lbs.}$$

Sometimes the force and the displacement are in the opposite directions. This situation gives rise to negative work. Note, in this case, the angle between the force and the displacement is a 180° angle. The cosine of 180° is negative one.

One example of negative work occurs when a body is lowered in a gravitational field. If a student carefully lowers a book weighing 15 pounds through a distance of 2 feet, we note that the displacement vector points downward and the force vector points upward.

$$W = FS \cos \theta$$

$$W = (15 \text{ lbs.}) (2 \text{ ft.}) \cos 180°$$

$$W = (15 \text{ lbs.}) (2 \text{ ft.}) (-1)$$

$$W = -30 \text{ ft.-lbs.}$$

Friction

We have referred to friction before. However, we will now try to quantify our ideas regarding friction.

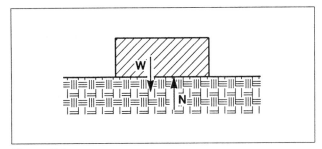

Figure 7-1.

COEFFICIENTS OF FRICTION		
MATERIAL	μ_{start}	μ_{slide}
Steel on Steel	0.15	0.09
Steel on Ice	0.03	0.01
Leather on Wood	0.5	0.4
Oak on Oak	0.5	0.3
Rubber on Dry Concrete	1.0	0.7
Rubber on Wet Concrete	0.7	0.5

Figure 7-2.

When a body rests on a horizontal surface or is dragged or rolled on a such a surface there is always contact between the lower body surface and the horizontal surface. This contact results in friction. Friction is work done as the surfaces rub against each other. This work heats the surfaces and always results in wasted work.

We need to define a force known as the **normal force**. A body resting on a horizontal surface experiences two forces, the downward force due to the gravitational pull of the earth on this body (the weight of the body), and the upward push of the surface itself on the body (the normal force).

The weight (w) and the normal force (N) are equal to each other.

There are three kinds of friction:
1. Starting friction
2. Sliding friction
3. Rolling friction

Starting friction is the friction present at the instant when a body, which has been at rest, just begins to move under the application of a force. Sometimes this instant when the body begins to slide is called "break away".

Sliding friction is the frition present as a body is sliding over another surface. Sliding friction is present when the surface of the body and the surface on which it slides are moving relative to each other.

Rolling friction is the friction between a rolling body and the surface on which it rolls. As in the case of sliding friction, the body and surface are moving relative to each other.

In all three cases, the friction equation is the same.

$$F = \mu N$$

The symbol "μ" (the Greek letter mu) is called the coefficient of friction.

Every pair of flat surfaces has two different coefficients of friction:

The coefficient of starting friction— μ_{start}
The coefficient of sliding friction—μ_{slide}

Some values for the coefficients of starting and sliding friction are given in figure 7-2.

We note that the coefficients of sliding friction are less than the coefficients of starting friction. This means that the force needed to **start** a body sliding is greater than the force needed to **keep** a body sliding with constant speed.

When we deal with a body that rolls over a flat surface, we have another coefficient of friction to consider: the coefficient of rolling friction.

The coefficients of rolling friction (μ_{roll}) are very small. Therefore, rolling friction is much smaller than either starting or sliding friction. Some values are:

Rubber tires on dry concrete	0.02
Roller bearings	0.001 to 0.003

EXAMPLE 7-D.

A steel body weighing 100 lbs. is resting on a horizontal steel surface. How many pounds of force are necessary to start the body sliding? What force is necessary to keep this body sliding at constant speed?

$$w = N = 100 \text{ lbs.}$$

$$F = \mu N$$

Force to start sliding motion

$$= (0.15)(100 \text{ lbs.}) = 15 \text{ lbs.}$$

Force to keep body sliding

$$= (0.09)(100 \text{ lbs.}) = 9 \text{ lbs.}$$

Energy

The concept of energy is one of the most important concepts in all of physical science. We often hear of energy sources, alternate energy, shortage of energy, conservation of energy, light energy, heat energy, electrical energy, sound energy, etc. What is the exact meaning of this word, **energy**?

Sometimes energy is defined as the "capacity to do work". This definition is only a partial definition. However, it has the advantage of immediately relating the concept of energy to the concept of work. These two ideas are intimately related to each other.

Energy is a quality that a body has after work has been done on this body. Once work has been done on a body of mass (m) this body has energy. The body can then do work on other bodies. Consider the following situation:

A body of mass (m) was resting on a horizontal air table. A player exerted a horizontal force (F) on this mass through a distance (S). Since the angle between the force and the displacement was a zero degree angle, the work done on this body was simply FS. At the instant the player removed his hand from the body we note two facts. The body accelerated while the force (F) was acting on the body and the body has acquired a velocity (v) during this time of acceleration (a). The body has moved through a distance (S) in time (t).

$$S = \frac{1}{2}at^2$$

Also note that the force (F) is related to the acceleration by the relation:

$$F = ma$$

We now look again at this body at the instant the force (F) has ceased acting. We note that work (W) has been done on this body, and that the body moves with speed (v).

$$W = FS = (ma)\left(\frac{1}{2}at^2\right)$$

$$W = \frac{1}{2}m(at)^2$$

Now we note that the speed obtained by the body during the time of acceleration is given by the equation:

$$v = at$$

Therefore, we can substitute v for at in the equation above.

$$W = \frac{1}{2}mv^2$$

The equation we have obtained is the defining equation for a quantity known as kinetic energy.

Usually, we use the symbol "KE" for kinetic energy.

$$KE = \frac{1}{2}mv^2$$

After the work has been done on the mass (m) it moves off on the frictionless air table with this kinetic energy. This body now is capable of doing work on other bodies that it contacts. For example, it probably will strike the edge of the table. When this happens this kinetic energy will be changed into other types of energy such as sound energy or heat energy.

We note that the initial kinetic energy of the mass (m) was zero. This is true because the body was initially as rest. We can say that the work done on the body is equal to the change in the energy of the body.

Gravitational Potential Energy

Another equally important situation where an agent easily can do work on a body (and thus give the body energy) occurs when the agent raises a body vertically in a gravitational field, at the surface of the earth.

In this case, the work done on the body again equals the force applied multiplied by the distance the body is raised.

$$W = FS$$

$$W = (\text{weight of body})(\text{distance raised})$$

We recall that w = mg. Also since the distance is a vertical distance we use the symbol "h" for height. In our discussion we will assume that the symbol "h" always represents the vertical distance of the body above the surface of the earth.

Therefore, we write:

$$W = mgh$$

Again we have a case where an agent did work on a body and the body has acquired "energy". This type of energy is known as gravitational potential energy, however, we usually symbolize it as "PE".

$$PE = mgh$$

If we neglect air resistance (which results in loss of energy to heat), we note that there is a conservation of kinetic and potential energy of a body moving in a gravitational field. As a body falls from a height (h) and moves closer to the surface of the earth, its potential energy decreases and its kinetic energy increases while it is falling. Therefore, there is an easy way of finding the speed of a falling body during any instant of its fall.

The units for energy are the same as the units for work, the Joule (J) in the metric system and the foot-pound in the English system.

EXAMPLE 7-E.

A body of mass 4 slugs is held by an agent at a distance of 6 ft. above the surface of the earth. The agent drops the body. What is the speed of the body when it is on the way down and at a distance of 2 feet above the earth's surface?

We note that the initial potential energy is equal to the sum of the kinetic and potential energies on the way down (wd).

$$PE_i = PE_{wd} + KE_{wd}$$

$$(4 \text{ slug}) (32 \frac{\text{ft.}}{\text{sec.}^2}) (6 \text{ ft.}) =$$

$$(4 \text{ slug}) (32 \frac{\text{ft.}}{\text{sec.}^2}) (2 \text{ ft.}) + \frac{1}{2} (4 \text{ slug}) v^2$$

$$192 \frac{\text{ft.}^2}{\text{sec.}^2} = 64 \frac{\text{ft.}^2}{\text{sec.}^2} + \frac{1}{2} v^2$$

$$128 \frac{\text{ft.}^2}{\text{sec.}^2} = \frac{1}{2} v^2$$

$$256 \frac{\text{ft.}^2}{\text{sec.}^2} = v^2$$

$$v = 16 \frac{\text{ft.}}{\text{sec.}}$$

EXAMPLE 7-F.

A body of mass, 10 kg, falls to the earth from a height of 300 m above the surface of the earth. What is the speed of this body just before it touches ground?

$$PE_i = KE_f$$

$$(10 \text{ kg}) (9.8 \frac{\text{m}}{\text{sec.}^2}) (300 \text{ m}) = \frac{1}{2} (10 \text{ kg}) v^2$$

$$2,940 \frac{\text{m}^2}{\text{sec.}^2} = \frac{1}{2} v^2$$

$$5,880 \frac{\text{m}^2}{\text{sec.}^2} = v^2$$

$$v = 76.7 \frac{\text{m}}{\text{sec.}}$$

The kinetic energy that the body has just before it reaches the ground immediately changes to sound energy and heat energy on impact. It may also "squash" any body in its path or make an indentation in the earth.

Momentum

The term "momentum" is often confused with kinetic energy, because momentum also depends on the mass of an object and its velocity. The definition of momentum is very simple:

$$\text{Momentum} = \text{mass} \times \text{velocity} = mv$$

Momentum is important when we discuss collisions. We will return to momentum and collisions in a later chapter.

Power

Power is the rate of doing work. The more rapidly a piece of work can be done by a person or a machine, the greater is the power of that person or machine.

We define power by the following equation:

$$\text{Power} = \frac{\text{work}}{\text{time}} = \frac{\text{force} \times \text{distance}}{\text{time}}$$

In symbols:

$$P = \frac{FS}{t}$$

In the English system the unit of power is the horsepower and in the metric system the unit is the watt.

In figure 1-6, we noted that there are conversion factors giving us information regarding these units.

$$1 \text{ Horsepower } = 550 \frac{\text{ft.-lbs.}}{\text{sec.}} = 33,000 \frac{\text{ft.-lbs.}}{\text{min.}}$$

$$1 \text{ Watt } = 1 \frac{\text{Joule}}{\text{sec.}}$$

$$1,000 \text{ Watts } = 1 \text{ kilowatt}$$

EXAMPLE 7-G.

An airplane engine weighing 4,000 lbs. is hoisted a vertical distance of 9 feet to install it in an aircraft. The time taken for this piece of work was 5 minutes. What power was necessary? Give the answer in ft.-lb./sec. and in horsepower.

$$P = \frac{FS}{t} = \frac{(4,000 \text{ lbs.}) (9 \text{ ft.})}{300 \text{ sec.}}$$

$$P = 120 \text{ ft.-lbs./sec.} \times \frac{1 \text{ HP}}{550 \text{ ft.-lbs./sec.}}$$

$$P = 0.218 \text{ HP}$$

EXAMPLE 7-H.

An elevator cab weighs 6,000 N. It is lifted by a 5 kW motor. What time is needed for the cab to ascend a distance of 40 m?

$$t = \frac{FS}{P}$$

$$t = \frac{(6,000 \text{ N}) (40 \text{ m})}{5,000 \text{ Watts}}$$

$$t = 48 \text{ sec.}$$

Alternate Form for Power

We can put our formula for power in another form by recognizing that $\frac{S}{t}$ is speed (v). This leads to the formula:

$$P = \frac{FS}{t} = F\frac{S}{t}$$

$$P = Fv$$

This form is particularly useful for obtaining an expression for the power output of a turbine engine. These engines are ordinarily rated in terms of the thrust which they produce. To obtain an expression for their power output it is necessary to multiply their thrust by the speed of the plane. This thrust power, which is usually expressed in units of horsepower (THP, thrust horsepower), can be obtained by multiplying the thrust in pounds by the speed in ft./sec. and dividing by 550 where the conversion 1 HP = 550 ft.-lbs./sec. is used. Thus:

$$\text{THP} = \frac{\text{thrust in lb.} \times \text{aircraft speed in ft./sec.}}{550}$$

Alternatively, we can take the speed of the aircraft in MPH and use the conversion 1 HP = 375 mi.-lbs./hr. to obtain:

$$\text{THP} = \frac{\text{thrust in lb.} \times \text{aircraft speed in MPH}}{375}$$

EXAMPLE 7-I.

A gas turbine engine is producing 5,500 lbs. of thrust while the plane in which the engine is installed is traveling 450 MPH. Determine the THP.

$$\text{THP} = \frac{(550 \text{ lbs.}) (450 \text{ MPH})}{375} = 6,600 \text{ HP}$$

It is important to note that while the thrust of a gas turbine engine may not vary much over a particular range of aircraft speeds, the power must be recalculated each time the plane changes its speed.

Reciprocating Engine Power

We will now direct our attention to the power delivered by a reciprocating engine. Since these engines are rated according to their power output, obtaining a formula for this output in terms of certain key variables will enable us to understand their design and operation better.

The work which is the source of power for the reciprocating engine comes from the expansion of hot gasses within a cylinder. This expansion forces a piston to move up and down within the cylinder. This motion is converted to a rotation by the action of a connecting rod on a crankshaft.

One full upward motion of the piston or one full downward motion of the piston is called a stroke. Most aircraft reciprocating engines operate on a four-stroke cycle called the Otto cycle in honor of the German physicist who developed it.

The four-strokes making up the cycle are the intake stroke, the compression stroke, the power stroke and the exhaust stroke. During the intake stroke, the piston moves down in the cylinder drawing the fuel/air mixture into the cylinder. The rotational motion set up in the propeller and crankshaft carries the piston upward compressing the fuel/air mixture. This is the compression stroke. It is in the next stroke, the power stroke, that the fuel/air mixture is ignited driving the piston down and generating the mechanical energy of the engine. In the upward exhaust stroke, the products of combustion are eliminated from the engine. The cycle then repeats.

The work done by the expanding gas during the power stroke can be calculated in the following way. The notation is as follows:

P = average effective pressure during the power stroke in PSI

L = length of the stroke in feet

A = area of the piston head or cross-sectional area of the cylinder in sq. in.

N = number of power strokes per unit time

K = number of cylinders

Since the force (F) on the piston can be written:

$$F = PA$$

The work done by the piston during the stroke is:

$$W = FL = PAL$$

This represents the work done by one cylinder in one power stroke. Since one revolution of the crankshaft corresponds to two strokes of the piston, and there is one power stroke per cycle (4 strokes), there is one power stroke per two revolutions of the piston. Let n equal the number of power strokes. Then:

$$n = \text{Number of power strokes}$$
$$= \frac{\text{number of revolutions}}{2}$$

Therefore, the total work output (W_{tot}) from a K cylinder engine in n power strokes is:

$$W_{tot} = PALnK \quad \text{or} \quad PLAnK$$

EXAMPLE 7-J.

Suppose we have a 12 cylinder engine (K = 12) with an average pressure (P = 155 PSI) during the power stroke, an Area (A = 28.3 in.^{2}, this corresponds to a diameter of 6 in.), and a stroke length (L = 8 in. = 0.667 ft.). Find the total work output in 50 revolutions (50/2 power strokes).

$$W_{tot} = (155 \text{ PSI}) (28.3 \text{ in.}^2) (0.667 \text{ ft.}) (50/2) (12)$$

$$W_{tot} = 878,000 \text{ ft.-lbs.}$$

If the crankshaft rotates at 50 revolutions per second, then the power output would be:

$$\text{Power} = 878,000 \text{ ft.-lbs./sec.}$$

Therefore:

$$\text{Power} = 878,000 \text{ ft.-lbs./sec.} \times \frac{1 \text{ HP}}{550 \text{ ft.-lbs./sec.}}$$
$$= 1,596 \text{ HP}$$

Indicated Horsepower

We can write an expression for what is called the indicated horsepower (indicated HP) of an engine.

$$\text{indicated HP} = PLANK/550$$
where N = the number of
power strokes per second

Another formula is:

$$\text{indicated HP} = PLANK/33,000$$
where N = the number of
power strokes per minute

The 33,000 represents the horsepower written in the form:

$$1 \text{ HP} = \frac{550 \text{ ft.-lbs.}}{\text{sec.}} \times \frac{60 \text{ sec.}}{1 \text{ min.}} = 33,000 \text{ ft.-lbs./min.}$$

EXAMPLE 7-K.

Given:

Effective pressure (P)	=	150 PSI
Stroke (L)	=	0.5 feet
Diameter of piston head	=	5.5 inches
RPM	=	2,000
Cylinders	=	12

The indicated HP is:

indicated HP = (150 PSI) (0.5 ft.) $[3.14 \times (2.75 \text{ in.})^2]$
(2,000/2) (12)/33,000 = 648 HP

Bernoulli's Principle

Bernoulli's Principle applies the ideas of work and energy and the conservation of energy to a mass of fluid (liquid or gas). Since it is not as easy to think of a mass of fluid as it is to think of a discrete body, the derivation of this principle requires some thought and effort.

It is worth the thought and effort, however, since this principle is the basic principle of the flight of heavier-than-air aircraft.

We review that the density of a fluid (ρ) is related to the mass and volume of the sample of fluid by the relation:

$$m = \rho V$$

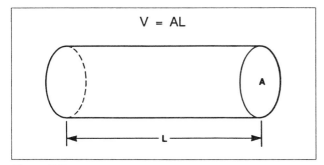

Figure 7-3.

We also review that the volume of a cylindrical shaped body is given by the product of the area of the base (A) by the length (L) of the body (see figure 7-3).

Recall that force is equal to the product of the pressure × the area:

$$F = PA$$

Recall also that:

$$\text{Work} = FS \cos \theta = \text{Change in Energy}$$

We will derive Bernoulli's Principle in the special case where there is no change in gravitational potential energy. This special case makes the derivation somewhat simpler and is the relation we need for applying the principle to an airplane wing where the upper and lower surfaces of the wing are at approximately the same height above the earth's surface. A "flowline" is the average path molecules of a fluid take as the fluid is in the process of flow. We consider "flowlines" of fluid as in figure 7-4.

The fluid flows from a region where the cross-sectional area is less (labelled with 1's in the diagram) to a region where the cross-sectional area is greater (labelled with 2's) in the diagram. We assume that the volume of fluid in the left cylindrical shape of fluid (labelled with 1's) is equal to the volume of fluid in the right cylindrical shape of fluid (labelled with 2's).

The fluid flows because of the fluid pressure. The left volume experiences a force from left to right while it moves forward from left to right. Positive work is done on the left volume. The right volume experiences a backward force as it tries to flow forward. The force on it is from right to left and it moves forward from left to right. Negative work is done on the right volume.

We note that the following notation is used for the pressure and velocity at the left and right volumes:

P_1	=	Fluid pressure on the left volume
v_1	=	Velocity of the fluid in the left volume
P_2	=	Fluid pressure on the right volume
v_2	=	Velocity of the fluid in the right volume
Also V	=	The common volume
And ρ	=	Density of the fluid

We now use the work-energy principle which says that the work done is equal to the change in energy.

Work Done = Change in Kinetic Energy

$$F_1L_1 + (-F_2L_2) = \frac{1}{2}mv_2{}^2 - \frac{1}{2}mv_1{}^2$$

Transpose the terms with 1's to the left member and the terms with 2's to the right member.

$$F_1L_1 + \frac{1}{2}mv_1{}^2 = F_2L_2 + \frac{1}{2}mv_2{}^2$$

$$P_1A_1L_1 + \frac{1}{2}V\rho v_1{}^2 = P_2A_2L_2 + \frac{1}{2}V\rho v_2{}^2$$

We know that the volume under consideration at the left is equal to the volume under consideration at the right. Therefore, we can say that:

$$V = A_1L_1 = A_2L_2$$

Therefore, we can write:

$$P_1 V + \frac{1}{2}\rho V v_1{}^2 = P_2 V + \frac{1}{2}\rho V v_2{}^2$$

We note that each term contains the volume (V). We can cancel it from each term.

$$P_1 + \frac{1}{2}\rho v_1{}^2 = P_2 + \frac{1}{2}\rho v_2{}^2$$

This equation is the form of Bernoulli's equation that we will use in our aircraft applications.

We note that this equation relates the pressure and velocity of a fluid in two different places (quantities with the 1's and those with the 2's). One example of the use of this equation occurs when the fluid is air and the two different places are the upper and lower surfaces of an airfoil such as an airplane wing, a propeller blade, or a helicopter rotor.

We also note that the relation between pressure and velocity is not a simple inverse proportion. However, as in any equation, the left and right members of the Bernoulli Equation must remain equal. Therefore, if the velocity of the air across an airfoil is increased the pressure is decreased and vice versa.

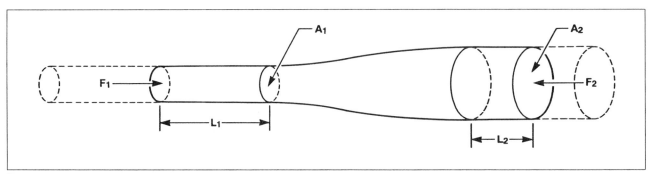

Figure 7-4.

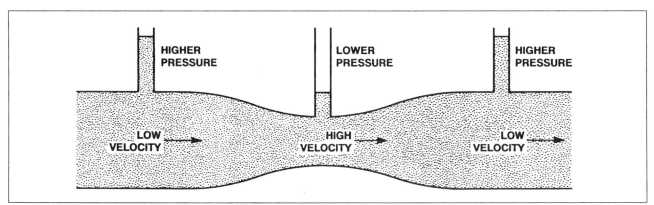

Figure 7-5.

An airfoil surface is designed in such a way that the air is forced to flow past the upper surface at a higher velocity than across the lower surface. It follows that the air pressure is less on the upper surface of the airfoil than it is on the lower surface. This higher pressure on the lower surface of the airfoil and lower pressure on the upper surface results in a net upward force called the lift.

In a later chapter, we will apply Bernoulli's Equation in some numerical examples. You may want to check the material in chapter 17.

Venturi Tube

A venturi tube is a tube constructed in such a way that the cross sectional area of the tube changes from a larger area to a smaller area and finally back to the same larger area. As a fluid flows through this tube the velocity of the fluid changes from a lower velocity to a higher velocity and finally back to the same lower velocity. We note that, if the rate (volume per time) of fluid flow is to remain constant, the fluid must flow faster when it is flowing through the smaller area.

A diagram of a venturi tube is shown in figure 7-5.

The height of the fluid column in the vertical tubes at the three places shown in the diagram, is an indication of the fluid pressure. As we expect from Bernoulli's Principle, the pressure is greater where the velocity is lower and vice versa.

Venturi tubes in different shapes and sizes are often used in aircraft systems.

Chapter VII Problems

1. How much work is done by a person in raising a 45 lbs. bucket of water from the bottom of a well that is 75 ft. deep? Assume the speed of the bucket as it is lifted is constant.

2. A tugboat exerts a constant force of 5,000 N on a ship moving at constant speed through a harbor. How much work does the tugboat do on the ship in a distance of 3 km?

3. A block is dragged over a rough, horizontal surface by a constant force of 78 lbs. acting at an angle of 25 ° above the horizontal. The block is displaced a distance of 45 ft. How much work is done by the worker?

4. A father has his 45-lb. son on his shoulders. He lowers the child slowly to the ground, a distance of 6 ft. How much work does the father do?

5. A big brother pulls his little sister a distance of 90 ft. on a sled. He exerts a force of 78 lbs. The rope makes an angle of 35 ° with the horizontal. How much work does he do?

6. An aircraft with a weight of 85,000 lbs. is towed over a concrete surface. What force must the towing vehicle exert to keep the airplane rolling?

7. It is necessary to slide a 200-lb. refrigerator with rubber feet over a wet concrete surface. What force is necessary to start the motion? What force is necessary to keep the motion going?

8. A 5.6 slug body has a speed of 43 ft. / sec. What is its kinetic energy? If its speed is doubled, what is its kinetic energy?

9. A 2 kg ball hangs at the end of a string 1 m in length from the ceiling of a ground level room. The height of the room is 3 m. What is the potential energy of the ball?

10. A body of mass 3 slug is a distance of 30 ft. above the earth's surface and is held there by an agent. The agent drops the body. What is the speed of the body just before it hits ground?

11. A baseball has a mass of 0.025 slug. It is held a distance of 7 ft. above ground by an agent. It is released by this agent and begins to fall to the ground. What is its speed when it is a distance of 4 ft. above ground on the way down?

12. An airplane engine weighing 12,000 N is lifted by a 4.5 kW motor a distance of 11 m. What time was needed?

13. A hand-powered hoist is used to lift an aircraft engine weighing 3,000 lbs. a vertical distance of 8 ft. If the worker required 4 minutes to do this job, what horsepower was developed by the man?

14. An elevator used to raise cargo must raise a load of 9,000 lbs. a vertical distance of 25 ft. in 50 seconds. What is the power requirement of the motor? Give your answer in both horsepower and kilowatts.

15. How long does it take a 5 kW motor to raise a load weighing 6,000 lbs. a vertical distance of 20 ft.?

16. A gas turbine engine is producing 6,500 lbs. of thrust in a plane traveling at 500 MPH. Determine the thrust horsepower.

17. If the plane in the preceding problem reduces its speed to 400 MPH, determine the new thrust horsepower.

18. A gas turbine engine is producing 5,500 lbs. of thrust in the plane in which it is installed. How fast must the plane travel (in MPH) to produce a THP of 7,000 HP?

19. *The gas turbine engine of a plane traveling at 400 MPH produces a thrust horsepower of 6,600 HP. How many pounds of thrust are produced by this engine?*

20. *The engines in the AVCO Lycoming 0-235 series have four cylinders with a piston diameter (bore) of 4.5 inches and a stroke of 3.875 inches. Fill in the missing values in the table below.*

	MODEL 0-235 C	MODEL 0-235 H	MODEL 0-235 L
indicated HP (HP)	115	109	_____
P (PSI)	_____	135	141
L (ft.)	_____	_____	_____
A (in.^{2})	_____	_____	_____
N strokes min.	1400	_____	1200
K	_____	_____	_____

Chapter VIII

Simple Machines and the Principle of Work

We defined work in chapter 7. The definition is as follows:

$$W = FD \cos \theta$$

The symbol for "distance" has been switched from s to D, to emphasize that we are dealing with **distances** in our treatment of simple machines.

The angle (θ) in this definition is the angle between the direction of the force vector and the direction of the displacement vector.

In this chapter, we will assume that in all the cases we will study the force and displacement vectors act in the same direction. This implies that the angle (θ) is a 0° angle and since the cosine of a 0° angle equals one, the equation for work becomes the simple equation:

$$W = FD$$

In this chapter, we will study six simple machines:

The lever
The pulley
The wheel and axle
The inclined plane
The screw
The hydraulic press

General Theory of All Machines

In discussing machines, we will assume that there is an object on which work is to be done. We will call this object the load. In most cases, it is required that the load be raised a certain distance in a gravitational field. For example, we wish to put cement blocks originally on the ground into the bed of a truck.

A machine is a device for doing this work. The input work is, by definition, the work done by the worker, that is, the force applied by the worker multiplied by the distance through which the worker's force acts. The output work is, by definition, the force that actually acts on the load multiplied by the distance the load is raised.

We note that one way to do work is to do it directly. For example, it is possible for the worker to raise each cement block directly to the truck bed. This is possible but can be difficult if each block weighs, say, 175 lbs.! In this case it would be better to use a machine since a machine usually decreases the force supplied by the worker and increases the distance through which his force acts.

In the equations which follow, the subscript "o" will stand for output and the subscript "i" will indicate input. We will use the following defining equations:

$$W_o = F_o D_o$$

$$W_i = F_i D_i$$

It is important to realize that there is no perfect machine. In our real world, on our earth, there is always some friction. We always have, at least, air resistance. In addition, there is friction due to the nooks and crannies that we would see if we inspected the surfaces of our machine parts with a high-powered microscope.

Because of the constant presence of friction the input work is always greater than the output work. Some of the input work is not useful work but serves to produce sound energy (a squeak), light energy (a spark), or heat energy.

We will use the symbol "W_f" to represent work lost because of friction.

$$W_i = W_o + W_f$$

We define two kinds of "mechanical advantage". The actual mechanical advantage (AMA) is the ratio of the output force to the input force. This actual mechanical advantage tells us how much easier it is for the worker. The ideal mechanical advantage (IMA) is the mechanical advantage that would exist if there were no friction in the machine. It is the ratio of input distance to the output distance.

$$AMA = \frac{F_o}{F_i} \qquad\qquad IMA = \frac{D_i}{D_o}$$

The ideal mechanical advantage of a machine can always be determined by measurements made on the machine itself.

The efficiency of a machine (Eff) is the ratio of the output work to the input work.

$$Eff = \frac{W_o}{W_i}$$

$$Eff = \frac{F_o D_o}{F_i D_i}$$

This equation can also be written with a complex fraction in the right member.

$$Eff = \frac{F_o / F_i}{D_i / D_o}$$

$$Eff = \frac{AMA}{IMA}$$

$$AMA = (Eff)\ IMA$$

The efficiency can be expressed as a decimal or as a percentage. For example, if the efficiency is calculated as 0.78, we can expressed it as 78%.

One final point should be made regarding efficiency. There is no machine that is 100% efficient. We always have some friction. However, sometimes we assume that there is no friction and that the machine is perfect or ideal! If a problem says that the efficiency is 100%, we are doing a make-believe problem. This kind of a problem is not meaningless, however, because it tells us the best that this machine can do. In this ideal case the AMA equals the IMA.

EXAMPLE 8-A.

A worker is able to raise a body weighing 300 lbs. by applying a force of 75 lbs. What is the AMA of the machine that he is using?

$$AMA = \frac{F_o}{F_i} = \frac{300\ lbs.}{75\ lbs.} = 4$$

A worker applied his force through a distance of 15 ft. The load is raised a distance of 2.5 ft. What is the IMA of the machine that he used?

$$IMA = \frac{D_i}{D_o} = \frac{15\ ft.}{2.5\ ft.} = 6$$

The actual mechanical advantage of a machine is 8 and the efficiency of this machine is 78%. What is the ideal mechanical advantage?

$$IMA = \frac{AMA}{Eff} = \frac{8}{0.78} = 10.3$$

A worker uses a machine to raise a load of 500 lbs. a distance of 2 ft. He does this by applying a force of 100 lbs. through a distance of 12 ft. What was the efficiency of the machine?

Method 1:

$$AMA = \frac{500\ lbs.}{100\ lbs.} = 5$$

$$IMA = \frac{12\ ft.}{2\ ft.} = 6$$

$$Eff = \frac{AMA}{IMA} = \frac{5}{6} = 83\%$$

Method 2:

$$W_o = (500\ lbs.)(2\ ft.) = 1,000\ ft.\text{--}lbs.$$

$$W_i = (100\ lbs.)(12\ ft.) = 1,200\ ft.\text{--}lbs.$$

$$Eff = \frac{W_o}{W_i} = \frac{1,000\ ft.\text{--}lbs.}{1,200\ ft.\text{--}lbs.} = 0.83 = 83\%$$

We will next consider six simple machines. In each of these cases the IMA is expressed, not as the ratio D_i / D_o, but in some other manner. We will study the geometry of each of these simple machines to determine how to express the IMA in some simple equation.

The Lever

Consider the diagram in figure 8-1. Note that the lever always pivots about some point called the fulcrum. The input force (F_i) is a downward force and, in our diagram, is applied at the right end of the lever. This input force gives rise to an upward force at the left end in our diagram. This upward force causes the load to be raised and is called "F_o".

In figure 8-2, note that the input force acts through a distance (D_i) and the load is raised a distance (D_o).

The distance from the input end of the lever to the fulcrum is called the input lever arm (L_i) and the distance from the output end to the fulcrum is called the output lever arm (L_o).

Recall that:

$$IMA = \frac{D_i}{D_o}$$

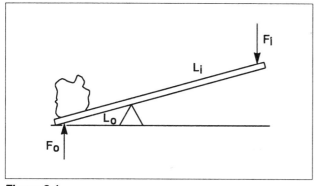

Figure 8-1.

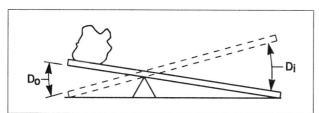

Figure 8-2.

However, figure 8-2 shows that the ratios of lever arms and distances are equal:

$$\frac{D_i}{D_o} = \frac{L_i}{L_o}$$

Since it is much easier to measure lever arms that the distances of rotation, we always use the ratio on the right hand side of the above equation to express the IMA of a lever.

Lever $\qquad IMA = \dfrac{L_i}{L_o}$

There are three classes of levers:

1st Class: The fulcrum is between the load and the applied force. Examples are the claw hammer, scissors, and crowbar.

2nd Class: The load is between the fulcrum and the applied force. Examples are the nutcracker and wheelbarrow.

3rd Class: The applied force is between the load and the fulcrum. An example is ice tongs.

In a third class lever, the IMA is less than one. There is no force advantage. However, there is a speed advantage. The work can be done in less time.

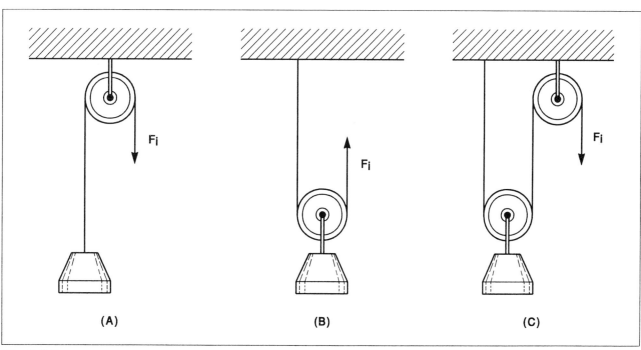

(A) (B) (C)

Figure 8-3.

The Pulley

Some pulleys are firmly attached to an overhead support while other pulleys move up or down with the load. We will refer to pulleys as "fixed" or "movable".

In figure 8-3A, we have shown a single fixed pulley. If a length of pulley cord (D_i) is pulled down by a worker, the load will be raised a distance (D_o). We see from the diagram that these distances equal each other. Therefore we conclude that the IMA of this type of pulley is one. For example, it would take 100 lbs. of force to raise a 100 lbs. load. The advantage of using this type of pulley is that the worker is able to pull **down** on the pulley cord and in this way an **upward** force is applied to the load. We say that a single fixed pulley is a "direction changer".

In figure 8-3B, there is a single movable pulley. A study of the diagram shows that D_i is always twice D_o. For example, if the load is to be raised 2 ft., the worker must pull in 4 ft. of cord. Note also that there are 2 strands supporting the load. The IMA of a single movable pulley is 2.

In figure 8-3C, there is a single movable pulley and a single fixed pulley. The fixed pulley again serves to change the direction of the input force. The IMA is still 2. Note also that there are again 2 strands supporting the load.

We conclude that the IMA of a pulley equals the number of strands supporting the load.

(Pulley)   IMA = the number of strands supporting the load

Several other examples of various types of pulley blocks are shown in figure 8-4.

The Wheel and Axle

Note that one cord is wrapped around the axle of radius (r). The load is attached to this cord. Another cord is wrapped around the wheel of radius (R). The worker applies his force to this second cord.

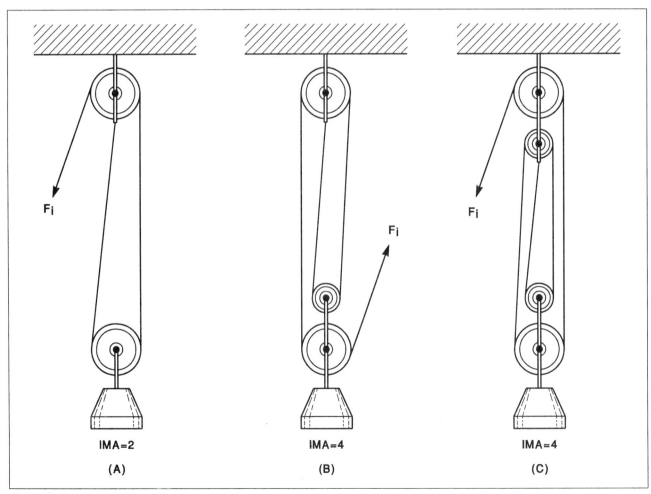

IMA=2
(A)

IMA=4
(B)

IMA=4
(C)

Figure 8-4.

Both wheel and axle turn together. This means that if the wheel rotates through one revolution the axle also turns through one revolution.

Let us suppose that the worker pulls in a length of cord equal to one circumference of the wheel (D_i). The load will be raised a distance equal one circumference of the axle, (D_o).

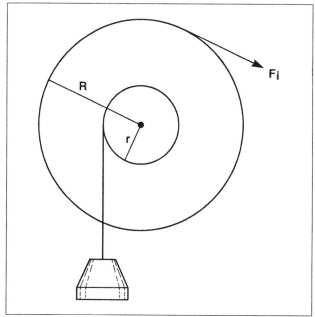

Figure 8-5.

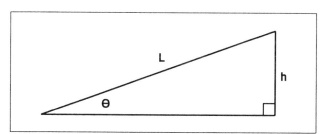

Figure 8-6.

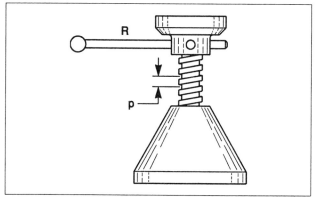

Figure 8-7.

$$IMA = \frac{D_i}{D_o} = \frac{2 \pi R}{2 \pi r} = \frac{R}{r}$$

Wheel and Axle $IMA = \frac{R}{r}$

The Inclined Plane

In the inclined plane shown in figure 8-6 we note that the worker slides the load up the incline. The input distance (D_i) is therefore equal to the length of the incline (L). The effect of this is that the load is raised a distance (h). This means that the output distance (D_o) equals h also.

$$IMA = \frac{D_i}{D_o} = \frac{L}{h} = \frac{1}{h/L}$$

We note that the sine of the angle of inclination (θ) is also h/L. Therefore, we can write the expression for the IMA as follows:

Inclined Plane $IMA = \frac{1}{\sin \theta}$

The Screw Jack

The pitch of the screw (p) is the distance between adjacent threads (see figure 8-7). As the handle is turned through one revolution, a distance given by $2 \pi R$, the load is raised a distance of one pitch.

Therefore, we have the relation:

Screw Jack $IMA = \frac{2 \pi R}{p}$

A screw jack has a great deal of friction. Therefore its efficiency is usually very low. However, the distance through which the input force acts in comparison to the pitch is usually very large. This gives a screw jack a large mechanical advantage.

The Hydraulic Press

A cross section of an hydraulic press is shown in figure 8-8. The small rectangles are cross sections of the circular input and output pistons. Usually, we talk about the areas of the input and output pistons (A_i and A_o). We note that the smaller of the two pistons is the input piston (radius = r) and, of course, the larger piston is the output piston (radius = R).

An hydraulic press is filled with some fluid (gas or liquid). This fluid exerts a common fluid pressure throughout the device.

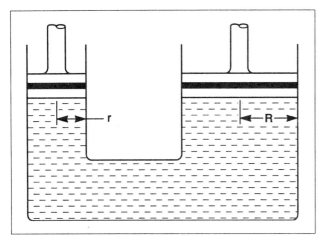

Figure 8-8.

As the smaller piston moves downward a distance (d_i) the larger piston moves upward a distance (d_o). We recall that the volume of a cylindrical shape is equal to the area of the circular base × the altitude. Also, a volume of fluid is transferred from the input (left) cylinder to the output (right) cylinder. The volume of fluid is constant since the pressure is constant. Therefore, we can write the equation:

$$\pi r^2 d_i = \pi R^2 d_o$$

We can cancel the common factor (π) and rearrange the equation. We obtain:

$$\frac{d_i}{d_o} = \frac{R^2}{r^2}$$

The left member of this equation is, by definition, the IMA. Therefore, the IMA is also equal to the right member of this equation. Thus, we can finally say that:

Hydraulic Press $\qquad IMA = \dfrac{R^2}{r^2}$

We have obtained equations for the IMA of each of the six simple machines. We will do an example of a typical problem dealing with machines. Note that any one of the six could be chosen as an example. In the problems that follow the example, be sure to use the correct formula for the IMA.

EXAMPLE 8-B.

The radius of the wheel in a windlass (wheel and axle) is 3.5 ft. and the radius of the axle is 0.27 ft. The efficiency of the machine is 60%. What load can be lifted by this machine by using a force of 75 lbs.?

$$IMA = \frac{3.5 \text{ ft.}}{0.27 \text{ ft.}} = 13.0$$

$$AMA = (Eff)(IMA)$$

$$AMA = (0.60)(13.0) = 7.8$$

$$F_o = (AMA)(F_i)$$

$$F_o = (7.8)(75 \text{ lbs.})$$

$$F_o = 585 \text{ lbs.}$$

EXAMPLE 8-C.

An inclined plane has a 32° angle of incline. A force of 50 lbs. is required to slide a 90 lbs. load up the incline. What is the efficiency of this machine?

$$IMA = \frac{1}{\sin 32°} = 1.89$$

$$AMA = \frac{90 \text{ lbs.}}{50 \text{ lbs.}} = 1.8$$

$$Eff = \frac{AMA}{IMA} = \frac{1.8}{1.89} = 0.95 = 95\%$$

Chapter VIII Problems

1. It takes a force of 85 lbs. to raise a body that weighs 239 lbs. What is the actual mechanical advantage of the machine that was used?

2. A load is raised a distance of 5.7 ft. by a force acting through a distance of 17.9 ft. What is the ideal mechanical advantage of the machine that was used?

3. What is the efficiency of a machine having an IMA of 6.9 and an AMA of 5.1?

4. A load weighing 130 lbs. is raised a distance of 4.1 ft. by a machine. The worker using the machine exerts a force of 52 lbs. through a distance of 12.3 ft. What was the efficiency of the machine?

5. A machine having an efficiency of 95% is used to raise a load weighing 500 lbs. a distance of 3 ft. A worker exerts a force of 100 lbs. to do this work. Through what distance must this 100 lbs. force act?

6. The radius of the wheel of a windlass is 4.0 ft. and the radius of the axle is 0.23 ft. The machine is 78% efficient. What force must be exerted to raise a load of 500 lbs. with this machine?

7. A jack screw has a pitch of 0.12 in. and the radius of the handle is 9 in. The efficiency of the machine is 35%. What force must be exerted to raise a body weighing 2,000 lbs.?

8. An inclined plane has an angle of inclination of 28°. The machine is 68% efficient. What load can be raised by a force of 70 lbs.?

9. The large piston of an hydraulic press has radius 1.5 ft. and the small piston has radius 0.32 ft. Assume that the machine is 100% efficient. What load can be raised by a force of 75 lbs.?

10. A pulley system has four strands supporting the load. A force of 55 lbs. is needed to raise a load of 200 lbs. What is the efficiency of this pulley system?

11. A nutcracker is used to crack a walnut. The distance from the fulcrum to the nut is 1.2 in. and the distance from the fulcrum to the hand is 5.1 in. The efficiency is 95%. The worker uses a force of 7.0 lbs. What force was applied to the walnut?

12. A light aircraft has a hydraulic braking system. Each rudder pedal is connected to a master cylinder which provides braking for one of the main landing gear wheels. Each master cylinder has a radius of ¼-inch. The cylinder on the wheel has a radius of 1.0 inch. If the system is 95% efficient and the pilot exerts a force of 55 lbs. on the pedal, how much force is exerted on the brake disc by the wheel cylinder?

13. A hydraulic press is used to raise an automobile in a repair shop. A force of 64.8 lbs. is needed to raise a car weighing 2,500 lbs. The efficiency of the press is 95%. If the radius of the input piston is 4.00 inches, what is the radius of the output piston?

14. A jack screw has a pitch of 0.14 inches and the radius of the handle is 11 inches. The efficiency of the machine is 38%. What force must be exerted to raise an automobile weighing 2,800 lbs.?

15. A pulley system has five strands supporting the load. A force of 51 lbs. is needed to raise a load of 200 lbs. What is the efficiency of this pulley system?

16. A can opener is used to open a can of paint. The distance from the fulcrum to the place where the lever fits under the lid of the can is 0.25 inches. The distance from the fulcrum to where the force is applied by the painter is 6.2 inches. The efficiency is 72%. If a force of 51 lbs. is needed to open the can, what force must be supplied by the painter?

17. The radius of the wheel of a windlass is 3.5 ft. and the radius of the axle is 0.34 ft. The machine is 75% efficient. What force must be exerted to raise a load of 450 lbs. with this machine?

18. An airline uses an inclined plane to load cargo. The load weighs 2,500 lbs. and a force of 800 lbs. is used. The efficiency is 76%. What is the angle of the incline?

19. A jack screw is used to raise an automobile to change a tire. The weight of the automobile is 3,000 lbs. A force of 25 lbs. is used. The efficiency is 34%. The handle has a radius of 13 inches. What is the pitch of the jack screw?

20. A wheel and axle is used to raise the anchor on the "dream boat". The anchor weighs 1,500 lbs. and a force of 300 lbs. is used. The efficiency is 65%. If the radius of the wheel is 23 inches, what is the radius of the axle?

21. An inclined plane is used to slide a body into the door of a warehouse. The body weighs 875 lbs. and a force of 200 lbs. is applied. The efficiency of the plane is 75%. What is the angle of the incline?

Chapter IX

Rotational Motion

In chapter 5, we discussed constant speed and accelerated motion in a straight line and derived four important formulas which will be reviewed below. In this chapter we will consider motion which takes place on a circular path. Such motion is very common in our complex society and we need to understand more about motion in curved paths.

Before we begin our discussion, we need to define a new unit for measuring angles, the radian (see figure 9-1).

A radian is defined as the central angle subtending a length of arc equal to the radius of the circle. A radian is approximately equal to 57.3°. The conversion factors for angle units are:

$$1 \text{ revolution} = 360°$$
$$1 \text{ revolution} = 2\pi \text{ radians}$$
$$2\pi \text{ radians} = 360°$$
$$1 \text{ radian} = 57.3°$$

Now let us consider a body (represented by a point) moving in a circular path. An initial reference line is shown in figure 9-2. As the point moves about the circle in a counterclockwise sense, a line drawn between the point and the center of the circle continuously sweeps out an angle. This angle can be measured in revolutions, radians or degrees. We call this angle the angular displacement of the point and use the Greek letter theta (θ) to represent this angular displacement.

If the point moves with constant speed it also has a constant angular velocity. That is, the line drawn from the point to the center of the circle sweeps out a definite number of revolutions, radians, or degrees each second or minute. The symbol used to represent angular velocity is the Greek letter omega (ω).

Angular velocity can be expressed in different units, such as,

radians	rev.	degrees
sec.	sec.	sec.
radians	rev.	degrees
min.	min.	min.

It is also possible that the point is not moving with constant angular velocity. It may be increasing or decreasing its angular velocity. When a record starts rotating on a turntable the angular velocity increases until it reaches a constant value. After the reject button is pushed the angular velocity decreases until the record comes to rest.

In both of the above cases we say that the point has an angular acceleration. The Greek letter alpha (α) is used for angular acceleration. Note that α is positive if the angular velocity is increasing and negative if the angular velocity is decreasing.

Angular acceleration can also be expressed in different units,

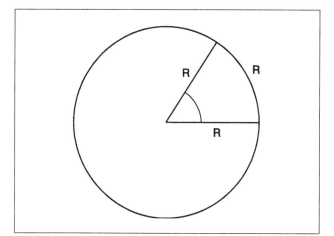

Figure 9-1.

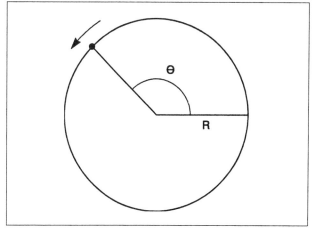

Figure 9-2.

$\dfrac{\text{radians}}{\text{sec.}^2}$	$\dfrac{\text{rev.}}{\text{sec.}^2}$	$\dfrac{\text{degrees}}{\text{sec.}^2}$
$\dfrac{\text{radians}}{\text{min.}^2}$	$\dfrac{\text{rev.}}{\text{min.}^2}$	$\dfrac{\text{degrees}}{\text{min.}^2}$

Now as a body moves in a circular path four similar equations hold as in the case of a body moving in a straight-line path. Both sets of equations will be shown below. It is important to re-memorize the equations for straight-line motion (see chapter 5). In this way the other four equations will also be known, since they are exactly analogous.

$$s = \frac{v_f + v_i}{2} t \qquad \theta = \frac{\omega_f + \omega_i}{t} t$$

$$v_f = v_i + at \qquad \omega_f = \omega_i + \alpha t$$

$$s = v_i t + \frac{1}{2} at^2 \qquad \theta = \omega_i t + \frac{1}{2} \alpha t^2$$

$$v_f^2 = v_i^2 + 2as \qquad \omega_f^2 = \omega_i^2 + 2\alpha\theta$$

Study these equations carefully and note that the set to the right, the "rotational analogs" are easily remembered if the left set is well known. We recall that the subscripts "i" and "f" indicate "initial" and "final".

These four rotational equations help us to solve many practical problems dealing with rotating bodies.

EXAMPLE 9-A.

A rotating machine part increases in angular velocity from 3 rev./min. to 35 rev./min. in 3.5 minutes. What is its angular acceleration?

We use the following equation and solve it for α.

$$\omega_f = \omega_i + \alpha t$$

$$\frac{\omega_f - \omega_i}{t} = \alpha$$

We now substitute our known values.

$$\alpha = \frac{35 \text{ rev./min.} - 3 \text{ rev./min.}}{3.5 \text{ min.}} = 9.14 \text{ rev./min.}^2$$

EXAMPLE 9-B.

A propeller starts from an angular velocity of 900 rev./min. and accelerates at 100 rev./min.² for 5 minutes. Through how many revolutions has it turned?

$$\theta = \omega_i t + \frac{1}{2} \alpha t^2$$

$$\theta = \left(900 \frac{\text{rev.}}{\text{min.}}\right)(5 \text{ min.}) + \frac{1}{2}\left(100 \frac{\text{rev.}}{\text{min.}^2}\right)(5 \text{ min.})^2$$

$$\theta = 5{,}750 \text{ revolutions}$$

EXAMPLE 9-C.

A propeller starts at 1,000 rev./min. and accelerates at 100 rev./min.² through 2,000 revolutions. What is its final angular velocity?

$$\omega_f^2 = \omega_i^2 + 2\alpha\theta$$

$$\omega_f^2 = \left(1{,}000 \frac{\text{rev.}}{\text{min.}}\right)^2 + 2\left(100 \frac{\text{rev.}}{\text{min.}^2}\right)(2{,}000 \text{ rev.})$$

$$\omega_f = 1{,}180 \frac{\text{rev.}}{\text{min.}}$$

We note that there is an acceleration of the body "in the path", called the tangential acceleration. The body is increasing or decreasing its speed of traversing the circle. We recall also that when a body moves in a circle there is also a centripetal acceleration, v^2/R, that is always directed **toward the center of the circular path**.

Thus when a body is increasing speed as it moves in a circular path there are two acceleration vectors, one tangent to the path, and the other directed to the center of the path! In figure 9-3, the body is increasing speed in the counterclockwise sense. The directions of the two acceleration vectors are shown.

Radian Measure

In figure 9-4, s is the length along the path. We would like to relate this distance to the size of the central angle (θ) and the radius (R) of the circular path. In our preceding discussion, the angle (θ) was measured in any of three different units, degrees, revolutions, or radians.

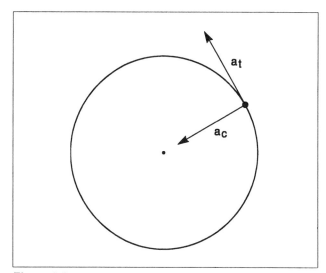

Figure 9-3.

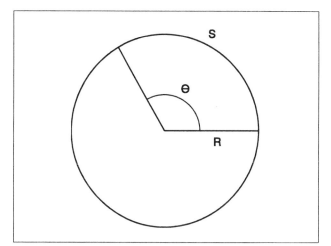

Figure 9-4.

The equation that relates s to θ and R is a very simple one if we limit the angular unit to radians. This equation is:

$$s = R\theta$$

We see that this equation is true if we look at figure 9-4. We note, by measuring, that the equation is satisfied. We also see that it would **not** be true if the angle θ was in revolutions or degrees.

We now have a new problem to deal with in our treatment of rotational motion. There is a limit to the units that may be used in this equation. We repeat that, for this equation, we must use radian measure. Also, any equation that is derived from $s = R\theta$ will have this same restriction.

Suppose that a body moves a small distance along the path and sweeps out a small central angle.

The usual mathematical notation for a very small quantity is the use of the Greek letter Delta (Δ).

$$\Delta s = R\Delta \theta$$

Let us divide both members of this equation by the time, (Δt) during which the motion occurred.

$$\frac{\Delta s}{\Delta t} = R \frac{\Delta \theta}{\Delta t}$$

We can write:

$$v = R\omega$$

If this velocity in the path is changing, there is also a change in the angular velocity. Assume that this change occurs in the small time interval (Δt).

We can write:

$$\Delta v = R \Delta \omega$$

Next we divide left and right members by Δt.

$$\frac{\Delta v}{\Delta t} = R \frac{\Delta \omega}{\Delta t}$$

The tangential acceleration (a_t) in the left member is the rate at which a body moving in a circular path is picking up speed **in the path**. It is equal to the radius times the angular acceleration (α).

We can write:

$$a_t = R\alpha$$

Let us summarize the three important equations we have derived:

$$s = R\theta$$

$$v = R\omega$$

$$a_t = R\alpha$$

All three of these equations require the use of radian measure. This means that:

θ must be in radians

ω must be in rad./min. or rad./sec.

α must be in rad./min.^{2} or rad./sec.^{2}

Note that the radian is called a "dimensionless" unit. We put it in or take it out for clarity!

EXAMPLES 9-D.

A car is moving on a circular racetrack of radius 150 ft. It sweeps out an angle of 200°. How far has it traveled?

We note that:

$$\theta = 200° \times \frac{6.28 \text{ rad.}}{360°} = 3.49 \text{ rad.}$$

$$s = R\,\theta$$

$$s = (150 \text{ ft.})(3.49 \text{ rad.})$$

$$s = 523 \text{ ft.}$$

EXAMPLE 9-E.

A race car is traveling at a speed of 176 ft./sec. (120 MPH) around a circular racetrack of radius 500 ft. What is the angular velocity of this car in rev./min.?

Use the equation:

$$v = R\,\omega$$

$$\text{or} \quad \omega = \frac{v}{R} = \frac{176 \text{ ft./sec.}}{500 \text{ ft.}}$$

$$\omega = 0.352 \frac{\text{rad.}}{\text{sec.}}$$

Note that we knew that the unit of our answer is rad./sec. and not rev./sec. since the equation we used always is in radian measure. The units in the right member of the second equation above actually come out as "nothing"/sec. We put in the radian unit in the numerator for clarity.

In order to find our answer in rev./min. we use the proper conversion factors.

$$\omega = 0.352 \frac{\text{rad.}}{\text{sec.}} \times \frac{60 \text{ sec.}}{1 \text{ min.}} \times \frac{1 \text{ rev.}}{6.28 \text{ rad.}}$$

$$\omega = 3.36 \text{ rev./min.}$$

EXAMPLE 9-F.

A race car is moving on a circular racetrack of radius 4,000 ft. It is increasing its speed at a rate of 15 ft./sec.^{2} What is its angular acceleration in rev./sec.^{2}?

We use the equation:

$$a_t = R\,\alpha$$

$$\alpha = \frac{a_t}{R} = \frac{15 \text{ ft./sec.}^2}{4,000 \text{ ft.}}$$

$$\alpha = 0.00375 \text{ rad./sec.}^2$$

We note that the unit is rad./sec.^{2} because the equation that we have used requires radian measure.

To obtain α in rev./sec.^{2}, we must use the standard conversion factor.

$$\alpha = 0.00375 \frac{\text{rad.}}{\text{sec.}^2} \times \frac{1 \text{ rev.}}{6.28 \text{ rad.}}$$

$$\alpha = 0.000597 \text{ rev./sec.}^2$$

Chapter IX Problems

1. A propeller starts from rest and accelerates at 120 rev./sec.^{2} for 4 seconds. What is its final angular velocity in rev./sec.? in rev./min.?

2. A rotating turntable starts from rest and accelerates at 5 rev./min.^{2} for 3 min. Through how many revolutions has it turned?

3. A helicopter main rotor starts from an initial angular velocity of 2 rev./min. and accelerates at 60 rev./min.^{2} while turning through 400 revolutions. What is its final angular velocity?

4. A propeller starts with an initial angular velocity of 2,000 rev./min. and decelerates at a rate of 5,000 rev./min.^{2} until it comes to rest. What is the time (in seconds) of this deceleration?

5. A helicopter tail rotor starts with an initial angular velocity of 15 rev./sec. and decelerates at a rate of 2.00 rev./sec.^{2} until it comes to rest. Through how many revolutions has the rotor turned while it comes to rest?

6. A plane is circling O'Hare in a circular pattern of radius 15,000 ft. It sweeps out an angle of 340°. How far has it traveled?

7. A plane is circling an airport in a circle of radius 5,000 ft. How far has it travelled after 4 revolutions?

8. A race car is moving on a circular track of radius 600 ft. It is traveling at a speed of 100 MPH. What is its angular velocity in rev./min.?

9. A race car is moving on a circular racetrack of radius 800 ft. It is accelerating at a rate of 10 ft./sec.^{2} What is its angular acceleration in rev./sec.^{2}?

Chapter X

Archimedes' Principle and Dirigibles

Archimedes was a Greek philosopher and mathematician who lived about 250BC. There is a story (maybe even true) about Archimedes that every physics student should hear. It goes as follows:

*The king who ruled Greece at that time asked his royal metalworkers to make him a gold crown. When the crown was delivered it was indeed beautiful. However, the king suspected that the crown was not pure gold. He did not want to destroy the crown but he wanted to know if he had been cheated. What he needed was some type of non-destructive evaluation (NDE dates back many years!). He asked Archimedes to solve his problem. Archimedes pondered the question. The density (mass/volume) of gold was well known. He knew of course how to determine the weight and mass of the crown by simple weighing. However, since the crown did not have a regular shape it was impossible to determine the volume by a mathematical calculation. The solution came to Archimedes one day when his servant filled his bathtub too full. As Archimedes stepped into his bath, he noticed that a volume of water equal to **his** volume overflowed! With a flash of insight he ran through Athens, stark naked, shouting "Eureka, Eureka, I have the solution!" The experiment was performed, the king was notified that his crown was not pure gold and the royal metalworkers lost their lives.*

The point of the above story is that a body submerged in a liquid displaces a volume of water equal to its own volume. A corollary is that a body that floats in a liquid displaces a volume of liquid less than its volume since some portion of the body is above the water level.

Archimedes' Principle

Archimedes' Principle is the principle that describes and explains the buoyant force that we all have experienced when we have tried to lift a body while it is under water or when we have floated ourselves or seen other bodies float.

In order to understand this principle let us consider the pressure that is present on any physical surface at a depth (h) below the surface of a liquid. Also assume that this upper surface of the liquid is exposed to the atmosphere. Let us also assume that the density of the liquid is ρ (rho).

In figure 10-1, assume that there is a "box" shaped object resting on the bottom of a large tank of liquid. The upper surface of this object has area (A) and is at a depth (h) below the surface of the liquid. This upper surface experiences the weight of the liquid in a column reaching from the upper surface of the "box" to the top surface of the liquid.

Let us calculate the weight of the liquid in this column. The volume of the column is the area of the column times the distance (h).

$$V = Ah$$

Recall also that density equal mass divided by volume and, therefore, mass equals density × volume.

$$m = \rho V$$

Therefore the mass (m) of the liquid in the column is:

$$m = \rho Ah$$

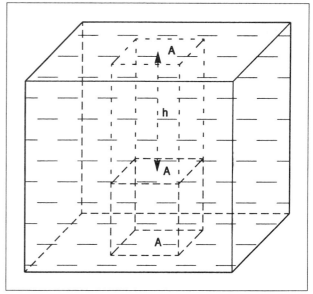

Figure 10-1.

73

Since weight is mass × g, we can calculate the weight (w) of the liquid in the column.

$$w = \rho Ahg$$

We also recall that pressure equals force divided by area.

$$P = \frac{F}{A}$$

Therefore, we are able to calculate the pressure on the upper surface of this "box" by dividing the weight of the liquid in the column, that is, the weight of the liquid pressing on the upper surface of the "box", by the area of this surface.

$$P = \frac{\rho Ahg}{A}$$

By cancelling the A's, we arrive at the equation that we desire:

$$P = \rho gh$$

This is a very important equation. It enables us to find the fluid pressure at a depth (h) below the surface of a liquid of density (ρ). This equation probably agrees with your intuitive sense. As we increase the depth below the surface of a liquid, we expect the liquid pressure to increase. We also expect that this liquid pressure would be greater in a liquid of greater density. What we have just said is that the pressure should be directly proportional to r and h. Note also that g is a constant. It is present in the equation because we have used the mass density rather than the weight density. Recall that figure 2-3 is a table of mass densities. You may need to refer to this table of densities as we do problems dealing with Archimedes' Principle.

When we say that the pressure below the surface of a liquid is given by ρgh, we mean that the pressure in any direction at a depth (h) is given by this expression. "In any direction" in the preceding sentence means up, down, right, left, front, back, or at any angle. At a depth (h) below the surface of a liquid, the molecules of the liquid are moving around and are bombarding any surface surrounded by the liquid. This bombardment by the liquid molecules is the cause of the liquid pressure. The greater the depth below the upper surface of the liquid, the greater is the effect of the bombardment by the moving liquid molecules.

Now let us suppose that a "box" shaped body is instantaneously thrust out from the hatch of a submerged submarine (see figure 10-2).

Three different possibilities exist. The "box" may rise to the surface. The "box" may stay at the same depth as the submarine. The "box" may sink to the bottom of the ocean.

In each case, we note that there is an upward pressure on the bottom surface of the "box" and a downward pressure on the top surface of the "box". There are also pressures to the right, left, front, and back but these pressures balance out each other. Since the bottom surface of the "box" is at a greater depth than the top surface, the upward pressure on the bottom surface of the "box" is greater than downward pressure on the top surface of the "box". This results in a net upward force. This net upward force is known as the buoyant force. We shall symbolize this buoyant force as "BF".

If the BF is greater than the weight of the "box", it rises to the surface. If the BF equals the weight of the "box", it stays at the same depth as the submarine. If the BF is less than the weight of the "box", the "box" sinks to the bottom of the ocean.

We have used a "box" and a submarine to try to describe this principle but obvious applications can be made to other bodies of liquid and to other objects.

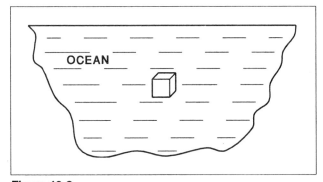

Figure 10-2.

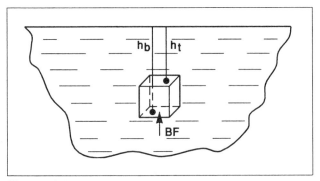

Figure 10-3.

Now we will calculate the size of the BF. Consider figure 10-3; remember that this is an instantaneous picture. The "box" will rise, stay at same depth, or sink. Let us call the depth of the top surface of the "box" h_t and the depth of the bottom surface of the "box" h_b.

Note also that the areas of the top and bottom surfaces of the "box" are both A. The volume of the "box" is given by the expression:

$$V = A\,(h_b - h_t)$$

since the expression in parentheses is equal to the height of the "box" (see figure 10-3).

Note that the upward force on the bottom surface of the "box" is:

$$F_b = A\,\rho\,g h_b$$

Also the downward force on the top surface of the "box" is:

$$F_t = A\,\rho\,g h_t$$

The net upward force (BF) is given by:

$$BF = F_b - F_t = A\,\rho\,g h_b - A\,\rho\,g h_t$$

$$BF = A\,\rho\,g\,(h_b - h_t)$$

$$BF = \rho\,g\,[A(h_b - h_t)]$$

$$BF = \rho\,g\,V$$

In this equation, note that ρ symbolizes the density of the liquid in which the "box" is submerged. Therefore, in the equation which follows, if m is the mass of the displaced liquid then V must be the volume of the displaced liquid.

$$BF = \frac{m}{V}\,g\,V$$

The V's will cancel in this equation if we note that the volume of the displaced liquid is equal to the volume of the "box". Therefore:

$$BF = mg$$

In this equation, m is the mass of the displaced liquid.

WEIGHT DENSITIES AT 68°F		
	N/m^3	LBS./FT.^{3}
LIQUIDS		
Water	9,807	62.4
Ocean Water	10,100	64.4
Benzene	8,620	54.9
Carbon Tetrachloride	15,630	99.5
Ethyl Alcohol	7,740	49.3
Gasoline	6,670	42.5
Kerosene	7,850	49.9
Lubricating Oil	8,830	56.2
Methyl Alcohol	7,770	49.4
Sulfuric Acid, 100%	17,960	114.3
Turpentine	8,560	54.5
SOLID METALS		
Aluminum	26,500	169
Cast Iron	70,600	449
Copper	87,200	555
Gold	189,300	1,205
Lead	111,200	708
Magnesium	17,100	109
Nickel	86,800	553
Silver	103,000	656
Steel	76,500	487
Tungsten	186,000	1,190
Zinc	70,000	446
Brass or Bronze	85,300	543
NONMETALLIC SOLIDS		
Ice	9,040	57.5
Concrete	22,600	144
Earth, Packed	14,700	94
Glass	25,500	160
Granite	26,500	169
WOODS		
Balsa	1,270	8
Pine	4,700	30
Maple	6,300	40
Oak	7,100	45

Figure 10-4.

Therefore, we note that the right member of this equation is equal to the weight of the displaced liquid since weight always equals mass × g.

We have now arrived at the traditional form of Archimedes' principle:

The buoyant force equals the weight of the displaced liquid.

We will look at several examples of the use of this principle to determine whether a given body will sink or rise to the surface of a liquid in which it is placed.

If a body has exactly the same density as the density of the liquid in which it is placed it will stay at any depth, actually the depth at which it is placed. This is a most unusual case. We will consider the other two cases with more detail.

In working examples and problems with Archimedes' Principle, it is convenient to define a new kind of density, the weight density. We will use the symbol "D" for it and will note the defining equation, weight density equals weight divided by volume.

$$D = \frac{w}{V}$$

$$\text{Also} \quad w = DV$$

$$V = \frac{w}{D}$$

Since the table of densities (figure 2-3) is a table of densities that list mass/volume, we will need a table of **weight** densities (figure 10-4).

When the term "water" is used we will assume that the meaning is clear water or lake water. If ocean water is meant we will specifically say "ocean water".

EXAMPLE 10-A.

A block of copper of volume 0.5 ft.^{3} is immersed in ocean water.

(a) What is the weight of this block?

(b) What is the BF on this block?

(c) What force would be needed to raise this block while it is immersed in ocean water?

    (a) The weight of the block can be found by using the equation:

$$w = DV$$

$$w = \left(555 \, \frac{\text{lbs.}}{\text{ft.}^3}\right)\left(0.5 \, \text{ft.}^3\right)$$

$$w = 277.5 \, \text{lbs.}$$

(b) The BF can be found by finding the weight of 0.5 ft.^{3} of displaced ocean water.

$$w = DV$$

$$w = \left(64.4 \, \frac{\text{lbs.}}{\text{ft.}^3}\right)\left(0.5 \, \text{ft.}^3\right)$$

$$w = 32.2 \, \text{lbs.}$$

Therefore, the BF = 32.2 lbs.

(c) The force needed to lift this copper block in ocean water is found by noting that the BF helps to raise the block. Therefore, only 277.5 lbs. − 32.2 lbs. of force would be needed.

We conclude that 245.3 lbs. of force would be needed to raise this block of copper while it is immersed in ocean water.

Archimedes' Principle Applied to Bodies that Float

A body will float in any liquid that has a weight density greater than the weight density of the body. For example a body of weight density 63.4 lbs./ft.^{3} would float in ocean water (D = 64.4 lbs./ft.^{3}) and sink in lake water (D = 62.4 lbs./ft.^{3}).

When bodies float they can float "high" or float "low". The ratio of the weight density of the floating body relative to the weight density of the liquid determines exactly how high or low a body will float.

In order to understand Archimedes' Principle as applied to floating bodies, let us again consider our submarine and imagine that a block of wood of weight density 48.3 lbs./ft.^{3} and volume 2 ft.^{3} is thrust out of the hatch of a submarine into the ocean water. We know intuitively that this block of wood will rise to the ocean surface.

The weight of the block is (48.3 lbs./ft.^{3}) (2 ft.^{3}) = 96.6 lbs. As long as the block is below the water surface (while it is rising to the top), it displaces 2 ft.^{3} of ocean water.

We know that:

$$BF = \text{wt. of displaced ocean water}$$
$$= (64.4 \text{ lbs./ft.}^3)(2 \text{ ft.}^3)$$

$$BF = 128.8 \text{ lbs.}$$

We can see why the block rises!

How far will the block rise? It will rise until the BF exactly equals its weight. In our example, it will rise until the BF has been reduced to 96.6 lbs. (the weight of the block). The BF will be reduced as the block emerges from the water. In our example, it will rise until 25% of the block's volume is above the water surface. It follows that 75% of 2 ft.^{3} or 1.5 ft.^{3} will be below the water surface. When this occurs the BF on the block is (64.4 lbs./ft.^{3})(1.5 ft.^{3}) equals 96.6 lbs. Note again that the BF equals the weight of the block while the block is floating.

In the preceding example, note that the ratio of the weight density of the block (48.3 lbs./ft.^{3}) to the weight density of the ocean water (64.4 lbs./ft.^{3}) was 0.75. We recall that 75% of the floating block was under water. This is generally true and makes a much easier procedure to determine how low a block will float in a given liquid.

In dealing with bodies that float, it is important to note that boats, made of materials more dense than water, are shaped in such a way that the total weight density is less than water. In order to understand this, consider the row boat with contents (people, lunch, fishing gear, etc.) shown in figure 10-6. Note that some of the boat (shown with dotted lines) is below the water surface. Suppose that the row boat floats in such a way that it displaces 8 cu ft. of lake water. The weight of the displaced water is 8 ft. (62.4 lbs./ft.^{3}) or 499 lbs. Therefore, the BF is 499 lbs. The boat and contents must weigh 499 lbs. to float at this level. If the boat weighs 150 lbs., the contents must weigh 349 lbs.

This is realistic (Daddy 200 lbs., son 75 lbs., lunch 25 lbs., fishing gear 49 lbs.).

One final comment should be made regarding submarines. Submarines cruising at a definite depth in ocean water have a total weight density equal to the weight density of ocean water, 64.4 lbs./ft.^{3} This means that the total weight of the submarine (metal shell, air, crew, load, ballast, etc.) divided by the total volume is 64.4 lbs./ft.^{3} The ballast used in submarines is ocean water. These vessels can take on water or pump out water. If the submarine wants to descend, it takes on water. If it wants to rise toward the surface it pumps out water.

EXAMPLE 10-B.

A block of oak (D = 45 lbs./ft.^{3}) is placed in a tank of benzene (D = 54.9 lbs./ft.^{3}). The oak floats since its weight density is less that the weight density of the benzene. What percentage of the oak will be below the surface of the benzene?

We find the ratio of the two weight densities.

$$\frac{45 \text{ lbs./ft.}^3}{54.9 \text{ lbs./ft.}^3} = 0.82$$

We conclude that 82% of the oak block will be below the surface of the benzene.

Hydrometers

A hydrometer is a device used for measuring the specific gravity of liquids, such as the battery fluid in an aircraft battery. This device works on the above principle. The "float" in a hydrometer floats higher or lower depending on the density of the battery

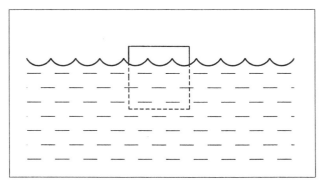

Figure 10-5.

Figure 10-6.

fluid. The "float" is calibrated to indicate this density. In this way, it is possible to determine the condition (charged or discharged) of the aircraft battery.

Archimedes' Principles as Applied to Dirigibles

In all of the above material, we have talked about Archimedes' principle as if it applied only to liquids. Since most of our experience with this principle is with liquids, it seemed easier to do this at first. However, it must now be emphasized that buoyant forces exist also with gases.

The obvious example is that of a hot air balloon or a lighter-than-air aircraft—a dirigible.

EXAMPLE 10-C.

The bag of a balloon is a sphere of radius 25 m filled with hydrogen of weight density 0.882 N/m^3. What total weight (in Newtons) of fabric, car, and contents can be lifted by this balloon in air of weight density 12.6 N/m^3?

We first calculate the volume of the spherical balloon by recalling that the volume of a sphere is given by:

$$V = \frac{4}{3} \pi R^3 = \frac{4}{3} (3.1416) (25 \text{ m})^3 = 65,450 \text{ m}^3$$

The weight of the hydrogen is found from the formula D V = w:

$$(0.882 \text{ N/m}^3) (65,450 \text{ m}^3) = 57,700 \text{ N}.$$

The weight of the displaced air is:

$$(12.6 \text{ N/m}^3) (65,450 \text{ m}^3) = 824,700 \text{ N}.$$

Since the weight of the displaced air is the BF we can say that:

$$BF = 824,700 \text{ N}$$

This BF must hold up the hydrogen, fabric, car, and contents. It follows that fabric, car, and contents weighing 767,000 N can be lifted by this balloon. Note that this number was obtained by subtracting 57,700 N from 824,700 N.

Usually balloons are not filled with hydrogen since hydrogen is explosive. Of course, since hydrogen is the lightest of all gases it is the most efficient. However, the danger of explosion outweighs this advantage. The next lightest gas is helium of weight density 1.74 N/m^3. Usually, balloons are filled with this gas.

Chapter X Problems

1. A solid aluminum object of volume 250 ft.^{3} is resting on the ocean floor. A salvage crew plans to raise this object. What force will be needed?

2. A solid steel body of volume 125 ft.^{3} is to be raised by a salvaging crew to the surface of a lake. What force will be needed?

3. What percentage of an iceberg is below the surface of the ocean?

4. A row boat and contents weighing 550 lbs. is floating on Lake Michigan. What volume of water does this boat displace?

5. A canoe is floating in such a way that it displaces 6 cu. ft. of lake water. If the canoe weighs 100 lbs., what is the weight of the contents of the boat?

6. A balloon is spherical in shape and has a radius of 40 ft. It is filled with helium (weight density 0.0111 lb./ft.^{3}) and is floating in air (weight density 0.0803 lb./ft.^{3}). What is the weight of the balloon (fabric, crew and contents)?

7. A Cessna 182 is fitted with pontoons for operation on lakes. As it taxies out for take-off the plane itself weighs 2,850 lbs., it has 40 gallons of gasoline in its tanks and the pilot and passenger together weigh 340 lbs. One gallon of gasoline weighs 5.67 lbs. What volume of water do the pontoons displace?

Chapter XI

Thermal Expansion of Solids and Liquids

The temperature of a body is a measure of the average kinetic energy of the molecules of that body. It follow that molecules of warm liquids and gases move around faster in their containers than molecules of cool liquids and gases. As a solid is heated its molecules vibrate faster about their equilibrium positions. As a result of this increased motion of molecules as they are heated, solids and liquids expand as the temperature is raised.

Linear Expansion

A rod of a substance will increase its length for a given temperature change. The increase in length depends on the original length of the rod, the temperature change, and the material of the rod.

We define alpha (α), the coefficient of linear expansion. Tables of values of alpha for various substances are found in handbooks of physics.

The formula is:

$$\Delta L = \alpha\, L_0\, \Delta T$$

In this formula,

L_0 = the original length of the rod
α = the coefficient of linear expansion
ΔL = the change in length of the rod
ΔT = the change in temperature

Area Expansion

Two-dimensional solid bodies also experience thermal area expansion. The formula is as follows:

$$\Delta A = 2\, \alpha\, A_0\, \Delta T$$

In this formula,

A_0 = the original area of the body
ΔA = the change in area of the body
ΔT = the change in temperature
α = the coefficient of linear expansion

Volume Expansion

Three-dimensional solid bodies experience volume expansion.

$$\Delta V = 3\, \alpha\, V_0\, \Delta T$$

V_0 = the original volume of the body
ΔV = the change in volume of the body
ΔT = the change in temperature
α = the coefficient of linear expansion

Liquids also experience thermal expansion. We introduce beta (β), the coefficient of volume expansion. There are also tables of the coefficients of volume expansion.

$$\Delta V = \beta\, V_0\, \Delta T$$

In this formula:

V_0 = the original volume
β = the coefficient of volume expansion

COEFFICIENTS OF LINEAR EXPANSION (α)	
SUBSTANCE	per F$^\circ$
Aluminum	13×10^{-6}
Brass	10×10^{-6}
Concrete (varies)	5×10^{-6}
Copper	9.4×10^{-6}
Glass (Pyrex)	1.6×10^{-6}
Ice	28×10^{-6}
Iron	6.6×10^{-6}
Lead	16×10^{-6}
Steel	11×10^{-6}

Figure 11-1.

ΔV = the change in volume

ΔT = the change in temperature

EXAMPLE 11-A.

A steel rail of length 140 ft. is laid down when the temperature is 20°F. What is the increase in length of this rail when the temperature is 95°F?

$$\Delta L = \alpha L_0 \Delta T$$
$$\Delta L = (11 \times 10^{-6}/F°) (140 \text{ ft.}) (75 \text{ F}°)$$
$$\Delta L = 0.116 \text{ ft.}$$

EXAMPLE 11-B.

An aluminum tank has volume 35 ft.^{3} What is the increase in volume of this tank when the temperature increases from 30°F to 90°F?

It should be noted that a solid block of a substance increases in volume as the body is heated. Also, a container has a bigger volume as the temperature of the container increases.

$$\Delta V = 3 \alpha V_0 \Delta T$$
$$\Delta V = 3 (13 \times 10^{-6}/F°) (35 \text{ ft.}^3) (60 \text{ F}°)$$
$$\Delta V = 0.0819 \text{ ft.}^3$$

EXAMPLE 11-C.

The manager of an airport accepts delivery of 1,000 gallons of gasoline on a cool evening when the temperature is 35°F. This gasoline completely fills a 1,000 gallon aluminum tank. A warm front moves in the next morning and the temperature rises to 95°F. How much gasoline will overflow? If the gasoline costs $1.25/gal., what is the loss to the airport?

For the gasoline:
$$\Delta V = (0.58 \times 10^{-3}/F°) (1,000 \text{ gal.}) (60 \text{ F}°)$$
$$\Delta V = 34.8 \text{ gal.}$$

For the tank:
$$\Delta V = 3(13 \times 10^{-6}/F°) (1,000 \text{ gal.}) (60 \text{ F}°)$$
$$\Delta V = 2.3 \text{ gal.}$$

The new volume of the gasoline is 1,034.8 gal. and the new volume of the tank is 1,002.3 gal.

We note that 32.5 gallons of gasoline will overflow!

$$\text{Loss} = \frac{\$1.25}{\text{gal.}} \times 32.5 \text{ gal.} = \$40.63$$

EXAMPLE 11-D.

A motorist puts 20.1 gallons of gasoline in his gas tank on a hot summer day when the temperature is 95°F. He uses 0.1 gal. in driving home. The temperature falls to 45°F that evening after a cool front has moved into the area. How many gallons are in his tank the next morning when he leaves for work?

$$\Delta V = (0.58 \times 10^{-3}/F°) (20 \text{ gal.}) (50 \text{ F}°)$$

$$\Delta V = 0.58 \text{ gal.}$$

There are 19.42 gallons of gasoline in his tank the next morning!

COEFFICIENTS OF VOLUME EXPANSION (β)	
LIQUIDS	per F°
Ethyl Alcohol	0.60×10^{-3}
Methyl Alcohol	0.66×10^{-3}
Benzene	0.69×10^{-3}
Gasoline	0.58×10^{-3}

Figure 11-2.

Chapter XI Problems

1. A 90 ft. aluminum rail is put in place on a hot summer day when the temperature if 89 °F. What is the decrease in length of this rail when the temperature is 35 °F?

2. A student purchases 4 gallons of benzene when the temperature is 80 °F in the hardware store. How many gallons does he have when he arrives at work where the temperature is 50 °F?

3. The volume of an aluminum tank is 1,550.0 gal. on a day when the temperature is 35 °F. It is completely filled with gasoline from a supply truck. The temperature rises to 70 °F when a warm front moves in. How many gallons of gasoline overflow?

4. A 150-ft. steel rail is put in place when the temperature is 35 °F. What is the increase in length of this rail when the temperature is 95 °F?

5. A brass plate has a 4.00 inch diameter hole in it. A rod of diameter 4.01 inches is to be threaded through this plate to produce an interference fit. This is to be done by increasing the temperature of the plate, passing the rod through the plate, and then allowing the plate to return to its normal temperature. What must be the temperature change of the plate?

6. The manager of an airport has a 2,000 gal. steel tank. He accepts delivery of gasoline when the temperature is 50 °F. The temperature goes up to 95 °F before the gasoline is sold. How many gallons overflow?

7. The manager of an airport has a 2,000 gal. steel tank. He accepts delivery of gasoline when the temperature is 50 °F. The temperature is expected to go up to 95 °F before the gas is sold. How many gallons of gasoline should he accept?

8. The manager of an airport accepts delivery of gasoline on a very hot day when the temperature of a 2,000 gal. steel tank is 95 °F. A cool front moves in and lowers the temperature to 50 °F before the gas is sold. At $2.25/gal., how much has the airport lost on this transaction?

9. A concrete bridge is laid down in sections with some space between sections to allow for expansion. The length of one section is 250 ft. The lowest recorded temperature in the area is –45 °F and the highest recorded temperature is 115 °F. How much space should the builders leave between each section?

10. The volume of an aluminum tank at an airport is 1,600 gal. on a day when the temperature is 40 °F. It is completely filled with gasoline from a supply truck. The temperature rises to 80 °F when a warm front moves in. How many gallons of gasoline overflow?

Chapter XII

Heat

We recall that temperature is a measure of the average kinetic energy, and therefore the average velocity, of the molecules of the substance whose temperature is being measured.

Heat is a measure of the total energy of molecular motion. The more molecules that are moving, the greater is the heat energy. Let us compare a teaspoon of water at 100°F with a cup of water at 50°F. The molecules of water in the teaspoon are moving faster than the molecules of water in the cup. However, since we have so many more molecules in the cup, the heat energy in the cup is greater than the heat energy in the teaspoon. If the teaspoon of water is placed on a large block of ice and the cup of water is also placed on this block of ice, the cup of water at 50°F would melt more ice than the teaspoon of water at 100°F.

There are definite units for measuring heat energy. The units are the Btu (British thermal unit) and the metric units, the large Calorie (written with a capital "C"), and the small calorie.

The definitions are:

1 Btu = the amount of heat needed to raise the temperature of 1 pound of water 1°F

1 Calorie = the amount of heat needed to raise the temperature of 1 kilogram of water 1°C

1 calorie = the amount of heat needed to raise the temperature of 1 gram of water 1°C

We note that the Calorie is the famous dietary Calorie. The body stores excess food as fat and we measure the Calories in a certain foodstuff by burning these foodstuffs and measuring the heat produced!

In the solution of heat problems, we will limit our discussion to the English system, since this is the system that is most often encountered in our society.

As heat is added to a body its temperature increases. However, the same amount of heat added to a piece of aluminum and a piece of copper will not produce the same temperature change. Aluminum and copper have different "specific heats".

A table of specific heats of various substances is found in figure 12-1. The important equation is the following:

$$Q = c \, w \, \Delta T$$

In this equation:

Q = heat gained or lost
c = the specific heat of the substance
w = weight of the body
ΔT = the temperature change

It is important to note that this equation deals with substances that are **not** changing their states of matter. Another equation will deal with heat added or lost as a body changes from one state (solid, liquid, or gas) to another.

SPECIFIC HEATS OF SOME SOLIDS AND LIQUIDS			
All Units Are Btu/lb.-F°			
SOLIDS		LIQUIDS	
Aluminum	0.212	Water	1.00
Brass	0.090	Ethyl Alcohol	0.58
Copper	0.094	Gasoline	0.5
Iron/Steel	0.11	Mineral Oil	0.5
Ice	0.48	Methyl Alcohol	0.60
Lead	0.031	Olive Oil	0.47
Silver	0.056	Paraffin	0.69
Tin	0.055	Petroleum	0.51
Zinc	0.094	Sea Water	0.93
GAS			
Steam	0.50		

Figure 12-1.

EXAMPLE 12-A.

How much heat must be supplied to raise the temperature of a 32-lb. aluminum fitting from 60°F to 90°F?

$$Q = c w \Delta T$$

$$Q = (0.212 \frac{Btu}{lb.\text{-}F°}) (32 \text{ lbs.}) (30°F)$$

$$Q = 204 \text{ Btu}$$

EXAMPLE 12-B.

How much heat is given up as 100 lbs. of sea water cools from 90°F to 50°F?

$$Q = (\frac{0.93 \text{ Btu}}{lb.\text{-}F°}) (100 \text{ lbs.}) (40 \text{ F°})$$

$$Q = 3720 \text{ Btu}$$

Heat Exchange

When hot bodies and cool bodies are mixed heat exchange occurs. The heat lost by the hot body equals the heat gained by the cold body:

$$\text{Heat Lost} = \text{Heat Gained}$$

On each side of this equation there is a $c w \Delta T$ term. In writing an expression for ΔT, we always express this change as the larger temperature minus the smaller temperature.

EXAMPLE 12-C.

If 5,000 lbs. of sea water at 100°F are mixed with 7,000 lbs. of ordinary water at 40°F, what is the final temperature of the mixture?

We note that, if the final temperature is T, the temperature 100° is more than T and the temperature 40° is less than T. Therefore the temperature change of the sea water is (100 − T) and the temperature change of the ordinary water is (T − 40).

$$\text{Heat Lost} = \text{Heat Gained}$$

In setting up the $c w \Delta T$ left and right members of the above equation, we will not include the units. However we will note that the weights must be in lbs. and the temperature changes in Fahrenheit degrees.

$$(0.93) (5,000) (100 - T) = (1.00) (7,000) (T - 40)$$

$$465,000 - 4,650 \, T = 7,000 \, T - 280,000$$

$$745,000 = 11,650 \, T$$

$$T = 63.9°F$$

Change of State

Sometimes adding heat to a substance does not increase its temperature. At certain critical temperatures, when heat is added, a substance will change its state of matter, rather than undergo an increase in temperature.

The typical example of such a substance is H_2O. The addition of heat at 32°F causes H_2O to change from the solid state (ice) to the liquid state (water). The addition of heat at 212°F causes H_2O to change from the liquid state (water) to the gaseous state (steam).

The heat supplied to cause a substance to change from the solid state to the liquid state is called the latent heat of fusion (L_f). Similarly, the heat required to change from a liquid to a gas is called the latent heat of vaporization (L_v).

Values of these latent heats are known for many substances and are listed in engineering handbooks. However, we will only work problems with H_2O, since this is the only substance that exists in all three states of matter for the temperatures and pressures common to our experience.

For H_2O:

$$L_f = 144 \frac{Btu}{lb.}$$

$$L_v = 970 \frac{Btu}{lb.}$$

For a change of state involving liquids and solids the equation is:

$$Q = w L_f$$

For a change of state involving gases and liquids the equation is:

$$Q = w L_v$$

We note that, at atmospheric pressure, the freezing point of water is 32°F and the boiling point of water is 212°F. This means that at temperatures

below 32°F the substance H_2O is in the solid state (ice). At temperatures **between** 32°F and 212°F, H_2O is a liquid (water). At temperatures **above** 212°F, H_2O is a gas (steam).

At **exactly** 32°F, the substance H_2O can be either a solid or a liquid. At this temperature, the solid is changing to a liquid if heat is being added or the liquid is changing to a solid if heat is being taken away.

At **exactly** 212°F, the substance H_2O can be either a liquid or a gas. At this temperature, the liquid is changing to a gas if heat is being added or the gas is changing to a liquid if heat is being taken away.

EXAMPLE 12-D.

How many Btu are necessary for changing 50 lbs. of ice at 32°F to 50 lbs. of water at 32°F?

$$Q = w L_f$$

$$Q = (50 \text{ lbs.}) (144 \frac{Btu}{lbs.})$$

$$Q = 7,200 \text{ Btu}$$

EXAMPLE 12-E.

How many Btu must be supplied to vaporize 40 lbs. of water at 212°F?

$$Q = w L_v$$

$$Q = (40 \text{ lbs.}) (970 \frac{Btu}{lbs.})$$

$$Q = 38,800 \text{ Btu}$$

Heat Exchange Involving Change of State

Heat exchange problems become more complicated if one includes bodies in the heat exchange that undergo a change of state. We will illustrate the method with examples.

EXAMPLE 12-F.

A 5-lb. block of ice at 32°F is placed in a vat containing 10 lbs. of water at 120°F. What is the final temperature of the mixture?

In setting up this problem we remember that the ice will first melt and form water at 32°F. Then this "ice water" must be raised to the final temperature.

We remember that the heat terms (Q terms) are either terms of the form $c w \Delta T$ or of the form $w L_f$.

We have the relation:

$$Q_{\text{needed for melting}} + Q_{\text{for heating ice water}} =$$
$$(5)(144) + (1.00)(5)(T - 32) =$$

$$Q_{\text{lost by hot water}}$$
$$(1.00)(10)(120 - T)$$

Next we simplify the equation:

$$720 + 5T - 160 = 1,200 - 10T$$

$$15T = 640$$

$$T = 42.7°F$$

EXAMPLE 12-G.

A vat contains 70 lbs. of water at 80°F. How many lbs. of ice at 32°F must be placed in this vat to reduce the temperature to 60°F?

We will let x represent the number of lbs. of ice.

$$Q_{\text{gained}} = Q_{\text{lost}}$$

$$144x + (1.00)(x)(60 - 32)$$
$$= (1.00)(70)(80 - 60)$$

$$144x + 28x = 1,400$$

$$172x = 1,400$$

$$x = 8.14 \text{ lbs.}$$

Heat Transfer

We know that heat flows through insulating materials from the warm side to the cool side. It is possible to predict how many Btu will flow through a given insulator in a given amount of time.

The equation is:

$$\frac{Q}{t} = \frac{kA\Delta T}{L}$$

The equation is less difficult than it seems at first. We will carefully define each symbol.

Q = heat flow in Btu

t = time in hours

A = the cross–sectional area of the insulation in square feet

ΔT = the temperature difference in F°

L = the thickness of the insulation in inches

k = the thermal conductivity of the material from which the insulation is made

EXAMPLE 12-H.

An outside wall of a house has total cross-sectional area of 2,000 ft.^{2} The thickness of the fiberboard insulation is 3 inches. The inside temperature is 70°F and the outside temperature is 20°F. What is the heat loss per hour through this outside wall?

$$\frac{Q}{t} = \frac{kA\Delta T}{L}$$

$$\frac{Q}{t} = \frac{(0.42 \text{ Btu–in.}/\text{ft.}^2\text{-hr.-F°})(2,000 \text{ ft.}^2)(50 \text{ F°})}{3 \text{ in.}}$$

$$\frac{Q}{t} = 14,000 \frac{\text{Btu}}{\text{hr.}}$$

Methods of Heat Transfer

Heat is transferred from one place to another by three different methods, conduction, convection and radiation. We will discuss each of the these methods of heat transference.

Conduction occurs when heat is transferred from one molecule to those molecules that are close by. Some substances conduct heat better than others. All metals are good heat conductors. If a metal spoon is used to stir a boiling liquid the handle soon becomes too hot to handle! Wood is a poor heat conductor. Therefore, wooden spoons are often used by cooks to stir their boiling liquids.

Convection occurs when quantities of fluids (gases or liquids) move from one place to another. Warmer fluids are less dense than cooler fluids and therefore they rise. Convection hot air systems are sometimes used to heat buildings. The air is heated by the heating units. The hot air rises in the system and automatically forces the cooler air

THERMAL CONDUCTIVITIES (Btu-IN./FT.^{2}-HR.-°F)	
Air	0.17
Corkboard	0.30
Cotton	0.54
Fiberboard	0.42
Foam Plastic	0.30
Glass Wool	0.27

Figure 12-2.

to fall down to the heating unit to be reheated. Convection currents of fluids occur whenever a fluid in a container is unequally heated. The warmer portions of fluid tend to rise in the container and the cooler portions of fluid tend to fall to the bottom of the container. This motion of fluid is called convection and the currents of fluid are called convection currents.

The third method of heat transfer is **radiation**. All bodies in the universe continuously emit a type of energy called electromagnetic radiation. This energy travels with the speed of light. Light itself, x-rays, cosmic rays, radio waves, and microwaves are all kinds of electromagnetic radiation. They differ in the wavelength and frequency of the emitted waves. A certain wavelength and frequency of this radiation is what we know as heat radiation. It lies in the infrared region of the electromagnetic spectrum. This radiation will be discussed in more detail in chapter 24. For now, we need to know that heat energy reaches us directly from our sun. It travels through a vacuum from the sun to the earth. As this energy reaches our earth it heats the surfaces on which it falls and causes the molecules of these surfaces to move more rapidly.

One example of radiation is the "greenhouse effect". As radiant heat energy enters a greenhouse or a closed automobile the radiation is reflected about within the closed building or automobile. As this happens the bodies within become very much warmer than the outside air. We are all aware that the steering wheel of a closed automobile in the summertime may become **very hot**. Sunshades decrease the effect because they allow less radiation to enter through the windshield and windows.

Chapter XII Problems

1. How much heat must be supplied to raise the temperature of 67 lbs. of ethyl alcohol from 32°F to 76 °F?

2. How much heat is given up as 780 lbs. of steel cool from 90 °F to 45°F?

3. If 0.5 lb. of ethyl alcohol (vodka) at 90 °F is mixed with 0.3 lb. of water at 32°F what is the final temperature?

4. If 3 lbs. of hot water at 200 °F are poured into a 1.5 lbs. aluminum container at 35°F, what is the final temperature?

5. A mixing faucet allows 3.0 gallons of hot water at 150 °F to enter a large sink in the same time that 2.0 gallons of cooler water at 50 °F enters the sink. What is the resulting temperature of the water in the sink? The weight density of water is 8.34 lbs./gal.

6. A mixing faucet is supplied with cold water at 45°F and hot water at 140 °F. The cold water tap supplies a flow is 0.5 gal./min. out of a total flow of 1.3 gal./min. through the faucet. What is the temperature of the resulting warm water?

7. If 79,900 Btu's were needed to vaporize a container of water at 212 °F, how many lbs. of water were in the container?

8. How much heat (in Btu's) must be supplied to melt 890 lbs. of water at 32°F?

9. How many Btu will be needed to vaporize 800 lbs. of water at 212°F?

10. If 500 lbs. of steam at 212°F condense, how many Btu will be given off to the atmosphere?

11. A 50-lb. block of ice at 32°F is placed in a container with 150 lbs. of water at 90 °F. What is the final temperature of the mixture?

12. A vat contains 100 lbs. of water at 95°F. How many lbs. of ice must be placed in this container to reduce the temperature to 50 °F?

13. If 3.00 lbs. of ice at 20 °F are placed in a large thermos bottle containing 6.00 lbs. of water at 95°F, how many lbs. of ice will melt?

14. The manager of an airport buys heat energy from a neighboring industry. Steam at 225°F is supplied to his building. If the return pipes return 1,000 gallons of water at 140 °F, how many Btu's of heat energy were supplied to the airport building? The density of water is 8.34 lbs./gal.

15. A 9-lb. block of ice at 32°F is placed in a vat containing 10 lbs. of water at 120 °F. How many lbs. of ice melt?

16. The manager of an airport building buys heat energy from a building close by. Steam at 220 °F is supplied to his building. If the return pipes return 1,500 gallons of water at 120 °F, how many Btu's of heat energy were supplied to the building? Give your answer in therms (1 therm = 10 Btu).

17. A house has an outside wall area of 3,000 ft.^{2} These walls are insulated with corkboard 4 in. thick. The inside temperature is 75°F and the outside temperature is 15°F. What is the heat loss per hour through these outside walls?

18. An ice chest used by a flight attendant is filled with 25 lbs. of ice as the flight leaves from O'Hare. The total area of the chest is 16 ft.^{2} The temperature in the ice chest is 32°F. The temperature in the cabin is 72°F. The insulation is fiberboard and is 0.311 inch thick. How many lbs. of ice melted during the first two hours of the flight? How many lbs. of ice are left after these two hours?

19. Ice is stored in a freezer at 32°F. The freezer is 2.3 ft. by 3.5 ft. by 4.8 ft. The insulation is 0.2 ft. thick and is made of foam plastic. If the electricity goes out and the outside temperature is 70 °F, how many pounds of ice will melt in two hours?

Chapter XIII

Sound

Sound waves are usually defined as pressure waves in air or in some other material medium. Sound waves originate in some vibrating body such as the oscillation of a person's vocal cords or the periodic rotation of a plane's propeller.

As the source of sound vibrates, the air surrounding the source is periodically compressed and rarefied (made less dense). This periodic change in the atmospheric pressure moves forward with a definite speed of propagation called the "speed of sound".

The speed of sound in air is dependent on the temperature of the air. This is not surprising since the molecules of air move faster in their random motion if the temperature is higher. Thus we should expect these pressure waves to move somewhat more rapidly in warmer air.

The relation giving the speed of sound at various temperatures is:

$$v = [1{,}087 + 1.1\,(F - 32)]\frac{\text{ft.}}{\text{sec.}}$$

In this formula, F represents the Fahrenheit temperature.

EXAMPLE 13-A.

What is the speed of sound at a temperature of 90°F?

$$v = [1{,}087 + 1.1\,(90 - 32)]\ \text{ft./sec.}$$

$$v = 1{,}151\ \text{ft./sec.}$$

Sound Waves and the Response of the Human Ear

If an ear and its eardrum are in the vicinity of a sound wave, the air which strikes that eardrum has a periodically changing atmospheric pressure. If the frequency of the sound is middle C (256 Hz), and the atmospheric pressure that day is 14.7 lbs./in.^{2}, 256 times each second the air pressure is slightly above 14.7 lbs./in.^{2} and 256 times each second the pres-

sure is slightly below 14.7 lbs./in.^{2} It should be emphasized that "slightly" means very small. The human ear is a remarkably sensitive instrument. It can detect air pressure variations as small as about 0.000000005 lbs./in.^{2}!

Intensity of Sound

For those working in the aviation industry it is important to understand something regarding the intensity of a sound wave.

The intensity level (IL) of sound waves is measured in a unit called the decibel (after Alexander Graham Bell).

The equation is:

$$IL = 10 \log \frac{I}{I_o}$$

In this equation IL is in decibels. The intensity, (I_o), is the intensity of the "threshold of hearing", the softest sound that the average human ear can detect. Also in the equation, I is the intensity of the sound we are measuring.

We note that:

$$I_o = 10^{-12}\ \text{Watts/m}^2$$

We also review that the $\log 10^n = n$.

EXAMPLE 13-B.

The intensity of a given sound is 10^{-5} Watts/m^2. What is the intensity level (IL) in decibels?

$$IL = 10 \log \frac{10^{-5}}{10^{-12}} = 10 \log (10^{-5})(10^{12})$$

$$= 10 \log 10^7$$

$$IL = 10\,(7) = 70\ \text{db}$$

It should be noted that 120 db is the "threshold of pain". Sound of this intensity is painful to the normal ear. If the ear is continuously subjected to sound of this intensity, ear damage and hearing loss can result.

Those who work in the aviation industry should take precautionary measures and wear ear protectors.

The intensity of sound decreases inversely with the square of the distance from the source of sound. Therefore, doubling the distance from a source of sound decreases the intensity to one-fourth of the previous value. A worker who is suddenly subjected to a very intense sound with unprotected ears should move as quickly as possible away from the source of this sound!

Sounds of sufficient duration and intensity can damage delicate inner ear structures and produce hearing loss that is not reversible. Workers in the aviation industry should be especially careful!

Sound Waves and Resonant Vibrations

Intense sound waves can cause resonant vibrations in pieces of equipment. There is a fundamental mode of vibration and a set of overtone vibrations (multiples of the fundamental) for any body that can vibrate. The frequencies of these vibrations are all natural frequencies for the given body. Vibrations of moving parts of equipment are often caused by "sympathic vibrations" to some impressed sound wave.

The Italian tenor, Enrico Caruso, had a powerful voice. Wine glasses have a natural frequency of vibration. As an attention getter at parties, Caruso used to sing the resonant note of a wine glass and cause the glass to vibrate with such amplitude that it would shatter! Try it sometime!

Supersonic Speeds

We recall that the speed of sound varies with the temperature. At 46°F, the speed of sound can be calculated as follows:

$$v = 1,087 + 1.1(46 - 32)$$
$$= 1,102 \text{ ft./sec.} \times \frac{1 \text{ MPH}}{1.47 \text{ ft./sec.}}$$

$$v = 750 \text{ MPH}$$

Jet planes can travel at speeds greater than the speed of sound. In this case, we have a source of sound, the plane, moving at a greater speed than the sound itself. The pressure waves of the sound all "pile up" and a very strong V-shaped pressure "bowwave" is produced. A sonic boom results as this strong pressure ridge reaches the earth.

The Mach number is the ratio of the speed of the plane (v_0) to the speed of sound (v). If a plane is traveling at 1,000 MPH and the temperature is 46°F, the Mach number is calculated in the following way:

$$\text{Mach Number} = \frac{v_0}{v} = \frac{1,000 \text{ MPH}}{750 \text{ MPH}} = 1.25$$

We say that the plane is traveling at Mach 1.25.

INTENSITY LEVELS OF SOME COMMON SOUNDS		
SOUND	INTENSITY (W/m^2)	INTENSITY LEVEL (db)
Rocket Engine	10^6	180
Jet Plane at Takeoff	10^3	150
Amplified Rock Music	10^{-1}	110
Riveting	10^{-3}	90
Elevated Train	10^{-4}	80
Busy Street Traffic	10^{-5}	70
Conversation in Home	10^{-6}	60
"Quiet" Radio in Home	10^{-8}	40
Whisper	10^{-10}	20
Rustle of Leaves	10^{-11}	10
Hearing Threshold	10^{-12}	0

Figure 13-1.

Chapter XIII Problems

1. What is the speed of sound at 75°F in ft./sec.? in MPH?

2. What is the speed of sound at –15°F in ft./sec.? in MPH?

3. If the temperature at 35,000 ft. is –40 °F, what is the speed of sound in ft./sec.? in MPH?

4. What is the intensity level of a sound having an intensity of 10^{-3} Watts/m^2?

5. What is the intensity level of a sound having an intensity of 10^{-7} Watts/m^2?

6. The temperature on a given day is 80 °F. A plane is traveling at 860 MPH. What is the Mach number?

7. If the plane in problem 6 continues to move at 860 MPH, but climbs to 36,000 ft. where the temperature is –40 °F, what is its Mach number at that altitude? Note that although the aircraft speed remains the same its Mach number has changed.

Chapter XIV

Review of Basic Trigonometry

The Theorem of Pythagoras

The Theorem of Pythagoras applies only to right triangles. Recall that a right triangle is a triangle in which one of the angles is 90°, and the other two angles are acute angles (angles less than 90°). The triangle in figure 14-1 is a right triangle. The right angle is labeled C, and the two acute angles are labeled A and B. The sides opposite each of the angles are labeled with the lower case a, b, and c. The side c (opposite the right angle) is called the hypotenuse. The sides a and b are called legs.

The Theorem of Pythagoras states that the sum of the squares of the legs is equal to the square of the hypotenuse.

In mathematical symbols, this relation is:

$$a^2 + b^2 = c^2$$

This formula can be solved for any one of the three quantities a, b, or c.

$$c = \sqrt{a^2 + b^2} \quad a = \sqrt{c^2 - b^2} \quad b = \sqrt{c^2 - a^2}$$

The Trigonometry of the Right Triangle

The definitions of the trigonometric functions of the acute angles of a right triangle are:

$$\text{sine } \theta = \frac{\text{opposite side}}{\text{hypotenuse}}$$

$$\text{cosine } \theta = \frac{\text{adjacent side}}{\text{hypotenuse}}$$

$$\text{tangent } \theta = \frac{\text{opposite side}}{\text{adjacent side}}$$

We abbreviate sine as "sin", cosine as "cos", and tangent as "tan".

If we apply these definitions to the above triangle, we obtain:

$$\sin A = \frac{a}{c} \qquad \cos A = \frac{b}{c} \qquad \tan A = \frac{a}{b}$$

$$\sin B = \frac{b}{c} \qquad \cos B = \frac{a}{c} \qquad \tan B = \frac{b}{a}$$

The Sum of the Angles of Any Triangle

The sum of the three angles of any triangle is always 180°. You can convince yourself of this fact by drawing several triangles, measuring carefully the three angles with a protractor, and adding the results. We can summarize this relation by writing the equation:

$$A + B + C = 180°$$

Solving Right Triangles

When we "solve" a triangle we find all of the unknown sides and angles. The above formulas can be used to solve right triangles.

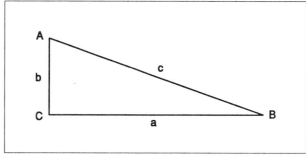

Figure 14-1.

EXAMPLE 14-A.

$$a^2 = c^2 - b^2$$

$$a^2 = (2.5)^2 - (2)^2$$

$$a^2 = 2.25$$

$$a = 1.5 \text{ in.}$$

$$\sin B = \frac{2}{2.5}$$

$$B = 53.1°$$

$$A = 90° - 53.1°$$

$$A = 36.9°$$

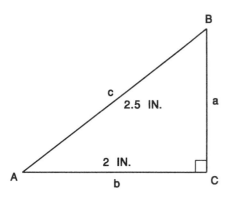

EXAMPLE 14-B.

$$B = 90° - 31°$$

$$B = 59°$$

$$\sin 31° = \frac{1.25}{c}$$

$$c = \frac{1.25}{\sin 31°}$$

$$c = 2.43 \text{ in.}$$

$$\tan 31° = \frac{1.25}{b}$$

$$b = \frac{1.25}{\tan 31°}$$

$$b = 2.08 \text{ in.}$$

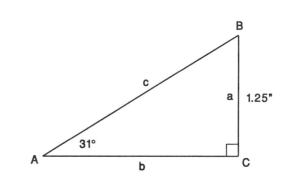

EXAMPLE 14-C.

A roadbed rises 205 ft. for each 2,250 horizontal ft. of road. Find the angle of inclination of the roadbed.

Call the angle of inclination A.

$$\tan A = \frac{205 \text{ ft.}}{2,205 \text{ ft.}} = 0.0911$$

$$A = 5.21°$$

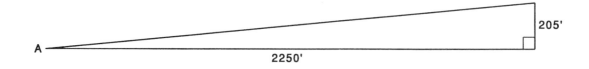

EXAMPLE 14-D.

Commercial airliners fly at an altitude of about 10 kilometers. They start descending toward the airport when they are still far away, so they will not have to dive at a steep angle. If the pilot wants the plane's path to make an angle of 4° with the ground, how far from the airport must he begin his descent?

Call the distance from the airport "d".

$$\tan 4° = \frac{10 \text{ km}}{d}$$

$$d = \frac{10 \text{ km}}{\tan 4°} = 143 \text{ km}$$

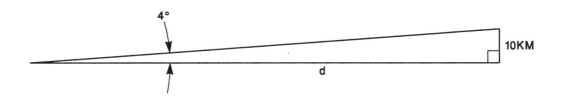

EXAMPLE 14-E.

How high up on the side of a building will a 10 meter ladder reach if the recommended safety angle of 75° is used?

Call the height above the base of the building, h.

$$\sin 75° = \frac{h}{10 \text{ m}}$$

$$h = 10 \text{ m} (\sin 75°) = 9.66 \text{ m}$$

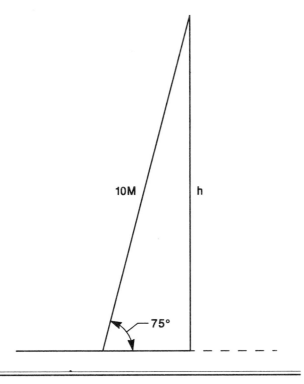

Introduction To the Use of the Sine and Cosine Laws

These laws apply to any triangle. However, if a triangle is a right triangle, it is much easier to use the Theorem of Pythagoras and/or basic right triangle trigonometry to find the unknown sides and angles of such a triangle. Therefore, usually the sine and cosine laws are used only for triangles which are not right triangles.

A general triangle is shown in figure 14-2. It is not a right triangle.

Note that the angles of this triangle are labeled A, B, and C. The sides opposite the angles are labeled a, b, and c respectively.

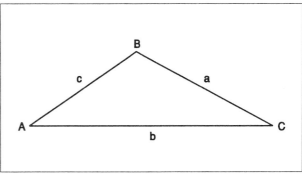

Figure 14-2.

The Cosine Law

The cosine law is used in two special cases:

1. It is used to find one of the angles of a triangle if the three sides are known.
2. It is used to find the third side of a triangle if the other two sides and the angle included between these two sides are known.

The cosine law is stated as follows (all three possible forms are given):

$$a^2 = b^2 + c^2 - 2bc \cos A$$

$$b^2 = c^2 + a^2 - 2ac \cos B$$

$$c^2 = a^2 + b^2 - 2ab \cos C$$

EXAMPLE 14-F.

The triangle shown here has three sides that are known.

We will use the cosine law to find one of the angles. Anyone of the three angles could be found by the cosine law. We choose to find angle A.

$$a^2 = b^2 + c^2 - 2bc \cos A$$

$$2bc \cos A = b^2 + c^2 - a^2$$

$$\cos A = \frac{b^2 + c^2 - a^2}{2bc}$$

$$\cos A = \frac{(4.5)^2 + (7)^2 - (4.8)^2}{2(4.5)(7)}$$

$$\cos A = 0.7335$$

$$A = 42.8°$$

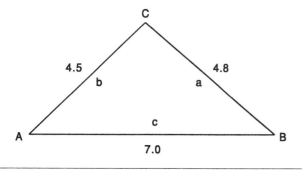

EXAMPLE 14-G.

The triangle in this case has two known sides and the angle between these two sides is also known. We use the cosine law.

$$a^2 = b^2 + c^2 - 2bc \cos A$$

$$a^2 = (6)^2 + (8)^2 - 2(6)(8) \cos 42°$$

$$a = 5.35 \text{ cm}$$

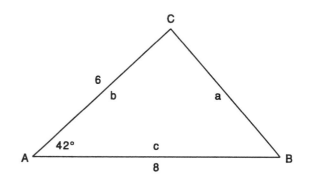

The Sine Law

The sine law is stated in the following equation:

$$\frac{a}{\sin A} = \frac{b}{\sin B} = \frac{c}{\sin C}$$

This mathematical expression is really three equations, since any two of the three quantities are equal to each other.

In words, this equation says that any side of a triangle divided by the sine of the angle opposite this side is proportional to any other side divided by the sine of the angle opposite that side.

The sine law is used for the solution of all triangles with the exception of the two cases described above where the cosine law must be used first.

Recall that supplementary angles are two angles whose sum is 180°. The sine of any two supplementary angles is the same number. For example, sin 30° = sin 150° = 0.5. Try this on your calculator for other pairs of supplementary angles, e.g. 20° and 160°, 35° and 145°, etc.

It is important to remember the above trigonometry when working with the sine law. For example, if you are finding the size of an angle that is obviously more than 90°, your use of the sine law will tell you that the value of this angle is a certain value when the true value of this angle is the supplement of this angle.

Example 14-I will clarify the above paragraph. The sine law will be used to solve a triangle when one of the angles of this triangle is more than 90°.

Let us summarize the method of solving (finding the unknown sides and angles) any triangle.

1. If the triangle is a right triangle, use the Theorem of Pythagoras and/or the definitions of the sine, cosine, and tangent.

2. If the triangle is not a right triangle, determine if all three sides are known or if two sides and the included angle are known. In either of these cases, use the Cosine Law first and then use the Sine Law.

3. If two sides and an angle, which is not the included angle, are known use the Sine Law for all of the unknowns.

4. If two angles and a side are known, use the Sine Law.

In some cases, a problem asks you to find only one unknown.

EXAMPLE 14-H.

In the triangle shown here, two angles and one side are known. We first find the third angle by noting that the sum of the angles of a triangle is 180°. Then we use the sine law to find the two unknown sides.

$$C = 180° - 35° - 75° = 70°$$

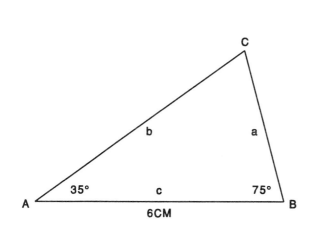

$$\frac{a}{\sin A} = \frac{c}{\sin C}$$

$$\frac{a}{\sin 35°} = \frac{6}{\sin 70°}$$

$$a = 6\,\frac{\sin 35°}{\sin 70°}$$

$$a = 3.66 \text{ cm}$$

$$\frac{c}{\sin C} = \frac{b}{\sin B}$$

$$\frac{6}{\sin 70°} = \frac{b}{\sin 75°}$$

$$b = 6\,\frac{\sin 75°}{\sin 70°}$$

$$b = 6.17 \text{ cm}$$

EXAMPLE 14-I.

$$\frac{4}{\sin 28°} = \frac{7}{\sin C}$$

$$\sin C = \frac{7}{4} \sin 28°$$

$$\sin C = 0.8216$$

If you ask your calculator for the size of the angle that has a sine of 0.8216, it will tell you that it is a 55.2° angle. This is obviously not the angle that is desired. The correct answer is the supplement of 55.2° or 124.8°. Be careful when dealing with angles that are greater than 90°.

The final answer for the size of angle C is:

$$C = 124.8°$$

The rest of the solution easily follows.

$$A = 180° - 28° - 124.8° = 27.2°$$

The length of side a can be found by using the Sine Law again.

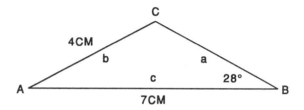

EXAMPLE 14-J.

Suppose that you are the pilot of a commercial airliner. You find it necessary to detour around a group of thundershowers. You turn at an angle of 25° to your original path, fly for awhile, turn, and intercept your original path at an angle of 37°, 63 km from where you left it. How much further did you have to go because of the detour?

From the fact that the sum of the angles of a triangle is 180°, the angle at B is known to be 118°. We use the sine law.

$$\frac{c}{\sin 37°} = \frac{63}{\sin 118°} \quad \text{and} \quad \frac{a}{\sin 25°} = \frac{63}{\sin 118°}$$

From these equations we obtain:

$$c = 42.9 \text{ km} \quad \text{and} \quad a = 30.2 \text{ km}$$

The detour was 73.1 km, a distance of 10.1 km more than the straight path from A to C.

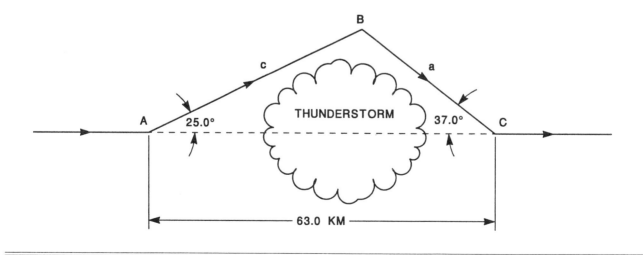

Chapter XIV Problems

1. A roadbed has angle of inclination of 7 °. If the road rises a distance of 350 ft., what is the slanting length of the road?

2. A ladder is placed next to a wall at the recommended safety angle of 75°. The horizontal distance from the base of the ladder to the wall is 2.5 ft. How long is the ladder?

3. A plane is flying at a altitude of 6,000 ft. The pilot wants the descent to be at an angle of 5° with the ground. How far from the airport must he begin his descent? Give your answer in miles.

4. A pilot flies 23.0 miles at an angle 73 ° N of E. How far east is he from his starting point? How far north is he from his starting point?

5. How high up on the side of a building will a 9.0 m ladder reach if the recommended safety angle of 75° is used?

6. A satellite is directly overhead one observer station when it is at an angle of 73 ° from another observer station. If the distance between the two stations is 875 km, what is the height of the satellite?

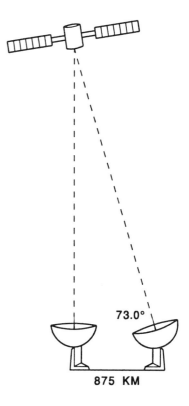

73.0°

875 KM

7. An astronaut approaches two satellites. Using radar, he determines that one of them is 7.3 km from him and the other is 12.4 km from him, and the angle between them (at the vertex) is 105°. How far apart are the satellites?

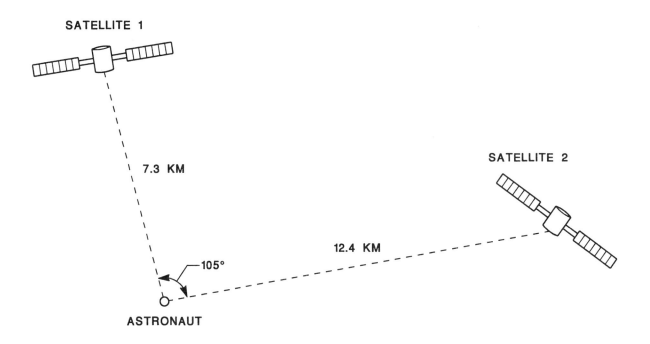

8. The pilot of a commercial airliner finds it necessary to detour around a group of thundershowers. He turns at an angle of 32° from his original path, flies for awhile, turns, and intercepts his original path at 20°, 72 miles from where he left it. How much farther did he have to go because of the detour?

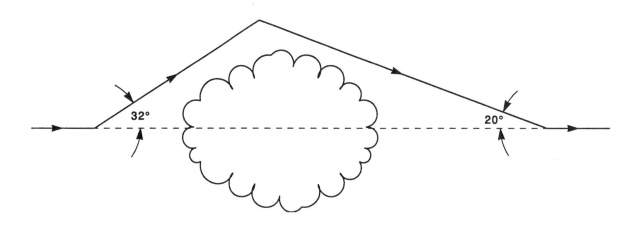

9. An astronaut approaching two satellites notes that one of them is 12 kilometers from him and the other is 14 kilometers from him. Futhermore, he notes that the angle formed by a line drawn from his position to one of the satellites and a line draw from him to the second of the satellites is 85°. Find the distance between the satellites.

10. *To welcome their returning war hero, the Pollutions give a parade. The parade goes between the cities of Tri, Ang, and Gel. These cities are at the vertices of an equilateral triangle (equal sides). The roads connecting them are straight, level, and direct, and the parade goes at constant speed with no stops. From Tri to Ang takes 80 minutes, from Ang to Gel takes 80 minutes, but from Gel back to Tri takes 1 hour and 20 minutes. How do you explain the discrepancy in times?*

11. *A beam of gamma rays is to used to treat a tumor known to be 6.8 centimeters beneath the patient's skin. To avoid damaging a vital organ, the radiologist moves the source over 10.2 centimeters.*
    (a) *At what angle to the patient's skin must the radiologist aim the gamma ray source?*
    (b) *How far will the beam travel through the patient's body before reaching the tumor?*

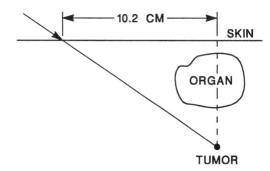

12. *The tallest free-standing structure in the world is the 553 meters tall CN Tower in Toronto, Ontario. At a certain time of day it casts a shadow 450 meters long on the ground. What is the angle of elevation of the sun at that time?*

13. *A triangle has sides of length 550 ft., 610 ft. and 755 ft. Find the number of degrees in the angle opposite the 755 ft. side.*

Chapter XV

Vectors

Definition of a Vector

A vector is any quantity that has both magnitude (size) and direction. A quantity that has only a magnitude is called a scalar.

Examples of scalars are temperature, area, and volume. Examples of vectors are displacement, velocity, force, and acceleration.

A vector is represented by an arrow. The length of the arrow indicates the magnitude of the vector and the direction of the arrow indicates the direction of the vector. If a quantity is a vector quantity, the letter that represents that quantity is underlined if it is hand-written on the board or on a paper. We will use bold-face print.

Vectors are represented on a coordinate plane (see figure 15-1).

Directions on such a coordinate plane are as follows:

Up	Positive
Down	Negative
Right	Positive
Left	Negative

The coordinate plane is divided into four quadrants. These four quadrants are labeled I, II, III, IV as in figure 15-1.

Also note that the horizontal line is called the x-axis and the vertical line is called the y-axis. The point, O, where the x-axis crosses the y-axis, is called the origin.

The vector in the diagram which follows is an example of a displacement vector. Note that it is 4.5 cm long and makes a 37° angle with the positive direction of the x-axis. It lies in the first quadrant. It is labeled **A**. The angle that the vector makes with the positive direction of the x-axis in a counterclockwise sense is called the reference angle. The reference angle of vector A is a 37° angle.

The Components of a Vector

If a line is drawn from the tip of a vector, perpendicular to the x-axis, the distance from the origin to the foot of this perpendicular is called the x-component of the vector. The y-component of the vector is defined in a similar manner, as the distance from the origin to a line drawn from the tip of the vector perpendicular to the y-axis. The x-component of the vector **A** is labeled A_x and the y-component is labeled A_y.

The components of the vector **A** are labeled in figure 15-2.

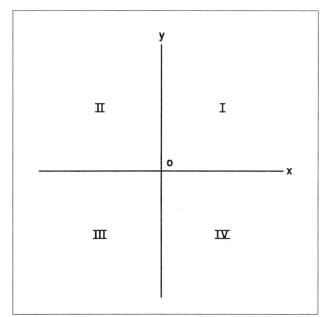

Figure 15-1.

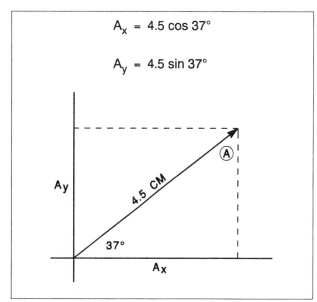

Figure 15-2.

It is very important to find the magnitude of the components of a vector. We need to do this in order to find the sum of vector quantities.

Our calculators are programmed to help us find the magnitude of vector quantities.

The x-component of any vector is found by multiplying the magnitude of the vector by the cosine of the reference angle.

The y-component of any vector is found by multiplying the magnitude of the vector by the sine of the reference angle.

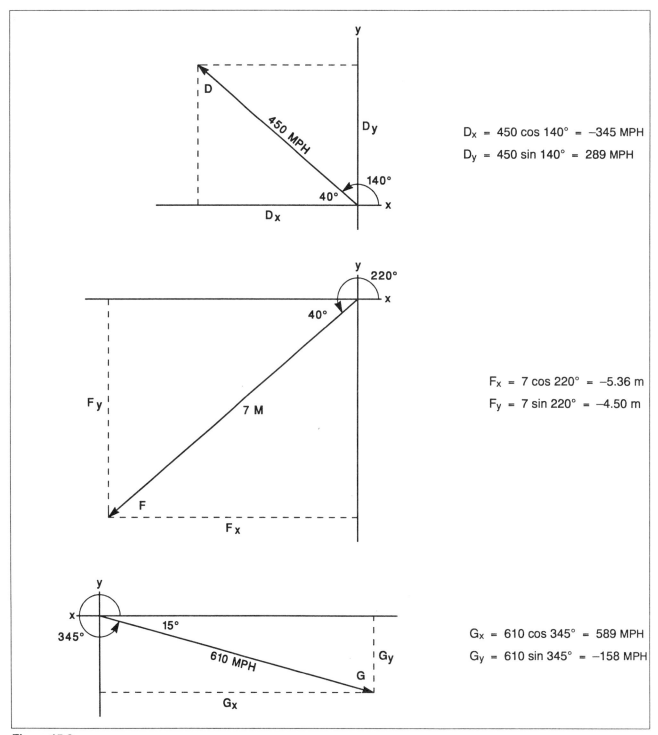

$D_x = 450 \cos 140° = -345$ MPH

$D_y = 450 \sin 140° = 289$ MPH

$F_x = 7 \cos 220° = -5.36$ m

$F_y = 7 \sin 220° = -4.50$ m

$G_x = 610 \cos 345° = 589$ MPH

$G_y = 610 \sin 345° = -158$ MPH

Figure 15-3.

The advantage of using our calculators in the above manner is that the calculator gives the correct signs of the vector components. If a vector is in the second quadrant, the x-component is negative and the y-component is positive. In the third quadrant, both components are negative. In the fourth quadrant the x-component is positive and the y-component is negative. The sign of a component is always determined by its direction, using the same convention as with the signing of the co-ordinate plane.

Most vectors must be drawn to scale because they are too big to be drawn on a normal sheet of paper, or because they are not displacement vectors and thus do not have an actual physical length. In particular, note that velocities are vectors and are added just as displacement vectors are added.

Vectors **D**, **F**, and **G** are shown in figure 15-3. In each of the following examples, the components of the vectors are found. It is necessary to determine the reference angle in each case. Recall that the reference angle is the angle the vector makes with the positive direction of the x-axis and rotating in the counterclockwise direction. Our calculators are programmed to find the components of any vector by this method. The x-component is found by multiplying the magnitude by the cosine of the reference angle and the y-component by multiplying the magnitude by the sine of the reference angle.

The above method for describing angles using a reference angle is very useful in developing a simple notation to describe vectors. The preceding

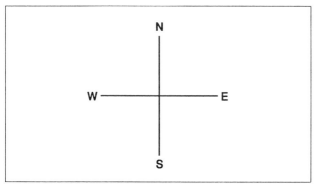

Figure 15-4. *In this notation, due east is at a 0 ° angle, north is at 90 °, west is at 180 °, and south is at 270 °.*

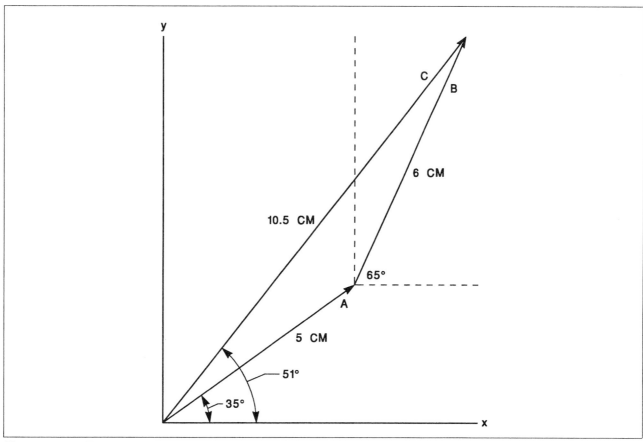

Figure 15-5. *This method shows the approximate sum as:* **C** : 10.5 cm, 51°

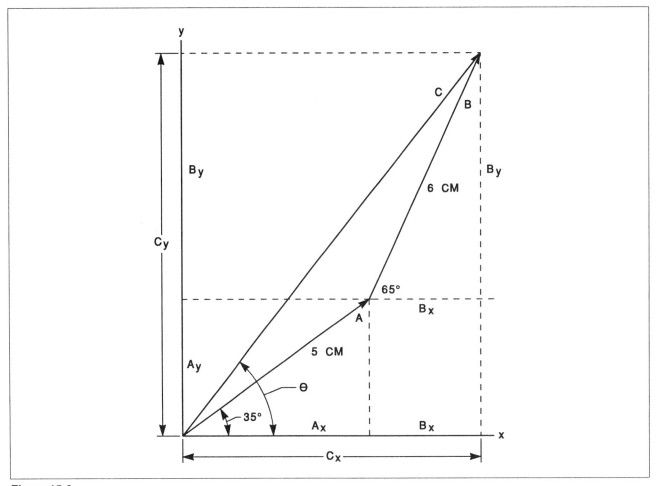

Figure 15-6.

three vectors could be described clearly even without a diagram. This would be done as follows:

D : 450 MPH 140°

F : 7 m, 220°

G : 610 MPH 345°

Sometimes the following notation (see figure 15-4) is also used, especially in the airline industry.

In should be noted that an alternate method sometimes uses 0° for due north, 90° for east, 180° for south, and 270° for west. We cannot use this notation since our calculators are not programmed in this manner!

Using the notation of the diagram in figure 15-4, we could describe vectors **D**, **F**, and **G** as:

D : 450 MPH, 40° N of W   or   50° W of N

F : 7 m, 40° S of W   or   50° W of S

G : 610 MPH, 15° S of E   or   75° E of S

The Addition of Vectors

Two vectors can be added to each other. This is best illustrated by the addition of displacement vectors. If one displacement is added to a second displacement, the result is a certain final displacement from the starting point. The actual distance from the starting point is not the sum of the two vector distances. The directions of the two vectors to be added are as important as the lengths in determining the final vector sum.

Consider the example shown in figure 15-5.

Two vector displacements are to be added. They are:

A : 5 cm, 35°

B : 6 cm, 65°

The sum vector (**C**) can be found by the "tail-head" method. In this method, the tail of the second vector (**B**) is placed at the head of the first vector, (**A**). The sum vector is found by drawing it from the tail of the first vector to the head of the second vector. The size of the sum vector can be found by measuring. The result found in this manner depends upon the care with which the figure is drawn. There are many possible sources of error: bent protractors, non-sharp pencils, warped rulers, sloppy diagrams, etc. The result is always approximate!

The Trigonometric Method for Adding Vectors

In the method described above, there is a built-in difficulty. The success of the method depends on the condition of the instruments used and the care with which the diagram is constructed. Some more exact method is needed. We will illustrate the trigonometric method by using the same example as above.

Study figure 15-6.

Note that:

$$A_x + B_x = C_x \qquad \text{and} \qquad A_y + B_y = C_y$$

The above two equations enable us to find the components of the vector (C) in an exact manner. For the example above we have:

$$A_x = 5 \cos 35° = 4.09$$
$$B_x = 6 \cos 65° = 2.54$$
$$C_x = 4.09 + 2.54 = 6.63 \text{ cm}$$

$$A_y = 5 \sin 35° = 2.87$$
$$B_y = 6 \sin 65° = 5.44$$
$$C_y = 2.87 + 5.444 = 8.31 \text{ cm}$$

The magnitude of the vector (C) and be found by using the Theorem of Pythagoras.

$$C = \sqrt{C_x{}^2 + C_y{}^2}$$

$$C = \sqrt{(6.63)^2 + (8.31)^2}$$

$$C = 10.6 \text{ cm}$$

A new diagram (figure 15-7) clearly shows the components of vector (C) and the angle (θ) that it makes with the positive direction of the x-axis.

Our final conclusion is that the vector (C) is 10.6 cm long and that it makes a 51.4° angle with the positive direction of the x-axis. Our results agree well with the diagrammatic method. However, this is often not the case if the diagram is not constructed very carefully. The trigonometric method is preferred whenever real accuracy is needed.

The trigonometric method is sometimes also called the component method, since it requires that we first find the x- and y-components of the two vectors to be added and, by adding, find the x- and y-components of the sum vector before we find the magnitude and reference angle of the sum vector.

This example was a special case since both components of both vectors were positive numbers. This will not be the case if the vectors to be added are not first quadrant vectors. If any one of the vectors to be added is not a first quadrant vector, great care must be taken to use the proper signs for all components.

The following example will clarify the procedure.

Add vectors **A** and **B** to obtain the sum vector, **C**.

$$\textbf{A} : 5 \text{ cm}, 150°$$
$$\textbf{B} : 7 \text{ cm}, 245°$$

$$A_x = 5 \cos 150° = -4.33$$
$$B_x = 7 \cos 245° = -2.96$$
$$C_x = -4.33 + (-2.96) = -7.29$$

$$A_y = 5 \sin 150° = 2.50$$
$$B_y = 7 \sin 245° = -6.34$$
$$C_y = 2.50 + (-6.34) = -3.84$$

It is important at this stage to draw a diagram to see the exact direction of the sum vector C. We note that the x-component of C is 7.29 units long and points left and that the y-component of C is 3.84 units long and points down. The two minus signs gave us the directions of these two components.

Next, we draw the diagram (figure 15-8). We do not include the signs since we have used the signs to tell us the proper directions of the component vectors.

We label the angle (θ) between the vector (**C**) and the x-axis. We can find the size of the angle (θ) by using the relation:

$$\tan \theta = \frac{3.84}{7.29} \qquad \text{and} \qquad \theta = 27.8°$$

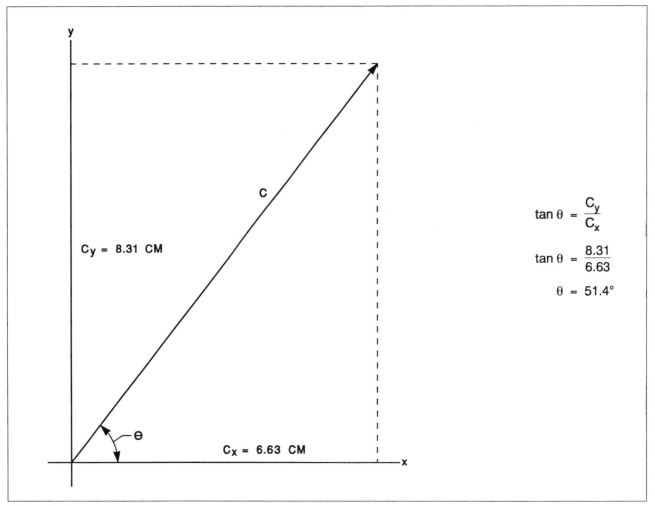

$$\tan \theta = \frac{C_y}{C_x}$$

$$\tan \theta = \frac{8.31}{6.63}$$

$$\theta = 51.4°$$

Figure 15-7.

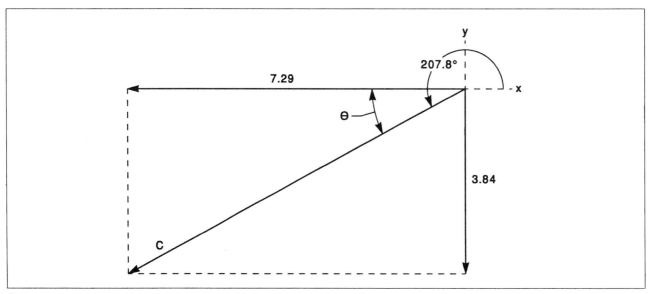

Figure 15-8.

From this value of θ, we find the reference angle to be 207.8°.

From the Theorem of Pythagoras, we find that:

$$C = \sqrt{(7.29)^2 + (3.84)^2} = 8.24 \text{ cm}$$

The final answer is written:

$$C : 8.24 \text{ cm}, 207.8°$$

This method can summarized as follows:
1. Find the reference angle of each vector to be added.
2. Find the x-component of each vector by multiplying its magnitude by the cosine of the reference angle.
3. Find the y-component of each vector by multiplying its magnitude by the sine of the reference angle.
4. Add the x-components to find the x-component of the sum.
5. Add the y-components to find the y-component of the sum.
6. Draw a diagram showing the x- and y-components of the sum.
7. Use the Theorem of Pythagoras to find the magnitude of the sum.

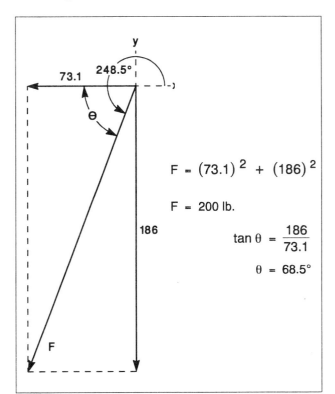

Figure 15-9.

8. Describe the direction of the sum vector by giving the reference angle. It is sometimes necessary to first find the size of the acute angle that the sum vector makes with the x-axis. From this acute angle, the size of the reference angle can be found.

Force Vectors

Another quantity that is a typical vector quantity is a force. We recall that a force is a push or a pull. A force has both magnitude and direction.

The addition of force vectors proceeds in an identical manner to the addition of displacement vectors. Recall that a vector is described by giving its magnitude and its reference angle.

EXAMPLE 15-A.

Add the force vectors:

$$F_1 : 50 \text{ lbs.}, 130°$$

$$F_2 : 150 \text{ lbs.}, 200°$$

$$F_3 : 200 \text{ lbs.}, 300°$$

In adding these three vectors, we first find the x- and y-components of these three forces. Then we add the x-components to find the x-component of the sum force. Next, we add the ycomponents to find the y-component of the sum force. Finally, we draw a diagram to find the magnitude of the sum and the reference angle of the sum force.

$$F_{1x} = 50 \cos 130° = -32.1$$
$$F_{2x} = 150 \cos 200° = -141$$
$$F_{3x} = 200 \cos 300° = 100$$

$$F_{1y} = 50 \sin 130° = 38.3$$
$$F_{2y} = 150 \sin 200° = -51.3$$
$$F_{3y} = 200 \sin 300° = -173$$

Next we add the x-components and the y-components.

$$F_x = -73.1 \qquad F_y = -186$$

We now know the x and y components of the vector sum of the three forces given. We need to draw a careful diagram to determine the magnitude of this

111

force and its direction (figure 15-9). We recall that the two negative signs tell us the directions of these components. The x-component is a component to the left and the y-component is a downward component. We use the Theorem of Pythagoras to determine the magnitude of the vector sum.

Our final vector sum can be expressed as:

F: 200 lbs., 248.5°

Recall also that if the direction of a vector to be added is given in the north, south, east, west notation, the first step in the addition of such vectors is to express the direction of each vector with the reference angle notation.

For example, a direction given as 30° S of W, should be expressed with reference angle 210°.

Chapter XV Problems

1. *Add the following vectors:* **A**: *45 m, 31° and* **B**: *66 m, 67 °. Call the sum vector* **C**.

2. *Add the following vectors:* **C**: *8.5 mi., 115° and* **D**: *12.6 mi., 215°. Call the sum vector* **E**.

3. *Add the following vectors:* **F**: *34.5 m, 165° and* **G**: *67.5 m, 295°. Call the sum vector* **H**.

4. *Add the following vectors:* **K**: *345 cm, 68 ° and* **M**: *435 cm, 180 °. Call the sum vector* **N**.

5. *Find the vector* **D**, *which is the sum of vectors* **A** *and* **B** *described below:*

   A: *56.7 cm, 47 ° N of W*
   B: *23.5 cm, 75° S of E*
   Hint: First find the reference angles of **A** *and* **B**.

6. *Find the sum of the following forces:*
   F₁: *700,000 lbs., South*
   F₂: *725,000 lbs., 15° W of N*

7. *Find the sum of the following three forces:*
   F₁: *711,000 lbs., 10 ° E of N*
   F₂: *160,000 lbs., West*
   F₃: *700,000 lbs., South*

8. *Find the sum of the following forces:*
   F₁: *342 N, 47 ° W of N*
   F₂: *782 N, 31° S of E*

Chapter XVI

Navigation Problems

An example of vector addition that is of great interest and importance to the aviation industry is shown in figure 16-1.

$$\mathbf{v}_{pa} + \mathbf{v}_{ag} = \mathbf{v}_{pg}$$

$\mathbf{v}_{pa}$ is the velocity of the plane relative to the air (airspeed)

$\mathbf{v}_{ag}$ is the velocity of the air relative to the ground (wind speed)

$\mathbf{v}_{pg}$ is the velocity of the plane relative to the ground (groundspeed)

Note that the vector sum of the airspeed and the windspeed is the groundspeed. The tail-head method has been used in the diagram below. Note that the plane is blown somewhat off course by the wind and that the pilot must adjust his heading according the wind velocity and direction.

In those cases where the vector triangle is a right triangle, the Pythagorean Theorem can be used. In such cases, the method is much more simple. Therefore, we will begin with this case.

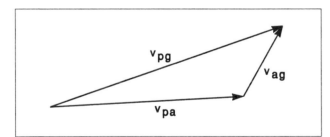

Figure 16-1.

EXAMPLE 16-A.

A pilot wishes to travel (relative to the ground) due north. There is a wind from the east at 40 MPH. The airspeed of the plane is 200 MPH. What is the groundspeed of the plane and in what direction should the pilot head?

In this example, there are several points that we must note carefully. First, we know both the direction and speed of the wind. Such information is available from the weather service.

For the vector that represents the groundspeed we know the direction but not the magnitude. We know the direction because we know exactly where on

the earth we want to go, that is, we have a definite destination on the earth! On the other hand we have the opposite information for the airspeed vector. We know the magnitude of this vector (the airspeed of the plane) but we must determine the direction of this vector. That is, we must determine the heading of the plane. This last bit of information is essential if the plane is to arrive at the desired destination.

The following steps should be followed in the following order for the solution of this type of problem:

1. Draw the groundspeed vector in the direction in which the pilot wishes to proceed.
2. Draw the windspeed vector with its head at the head of the groundspeed vector.
3. Draw the airspeed vector from the tail of the groundspeed vector to the tail of the windspeed vector.

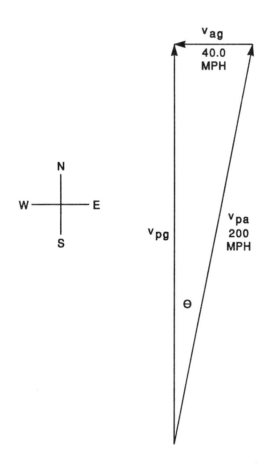

We will solve the problem using these three steps in the order given.

Note that we have drawn the groundspeed vector due north. The wind vector is drawn to the west (it was an east wind). We have made this wind vector significantly shorter than the groundspeed vector since the windspeed is usually much smaller than the groundspeed. Note that the heads of these two vectors are **together**. Finally, we have drawn a vector from the tail of the first vector to the tail of the second vector drawn.

Note that for the groundspeed vector we know the direction but not the magnitude.

Note that for the airspeed vector we know the magnitude but not the direction.

$$v_{pg} = \sqrt{200^2 - 40^2} = 196 \text{ MPH}$$

$$\sin \theta = \frac{40}{200} \quad \text{and therefore, } \theta = 11.5°$$

The groundspeed of the plane is 196 MPH and the pilot should head 11.5° E of N.

More Complicated Navigation Problems

If the vector triangle is not a right triangle, the method is the same. However, in this case, it will be necessary to use the sine law to determine the two unknowns. In addition, the "Z" rule will often be helpful in determining the number of degrees in one of the interior angles of the vector triangle.

EXAMPLE 16-B.

A pilot wishes to proceed in a direction 55° N of E (35° E of N). There is a wind from the west at 35 MPH. The airspeed of the plane is 215 MPH. What is the groundspeed of the plane and in what direction should the pilot head?

Use the Z rule to find the 55° interior angle of the triangle.

$$\frac{35}{\sin \theta} = \frac{215}{\sin 55°}$$

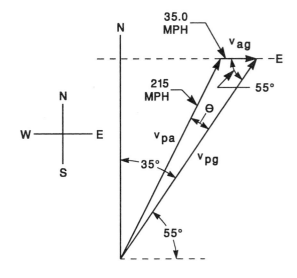

$$\sin \theta = \frac{35}{215} \sin 55°$$

$$\theta = 7.7°$$

$$35° - 7.7° = 27.3° \text{ (the heading of the plane)}$$

The third interior angle of the triangle can now be found. It is 117.3°. Now the sine law can be used again.

$$\frac{215}{\sin 55°} = \frac{v_{pg}}{\sin 117.3°}$$

$$v_{pg} = 233 \text{ MPH}$$

The groundspeed of the plane is 233 MPH, and the pilot should head 27.3° E of N.

Each navigation problem dealing with a vector triangle which is not a right triangle must be handled carefully. A clear diagram **must** be drawn. The size of the angle between the wind vector and the groundspeed vector can always be found. The Z rule often helps. Another theorem of plane geometry is sometimes helpful. This theorem states that vertical angles (two angles lying on opposite sides of two intersecting lines) are equal. This rule is sometimes referred to as the "X" rule. Recall also that two angles lying on the same side of two intersecting lines always add up to 180°.

Chapter XVI Problems

1. A pilot wishes to travel due north. There is a wind from the west at 30 MPH. The airspeed of the plane is 195 MPH. What is the groundspeed of the plane and in what direction should the pilot head?

2. A pilot wishes to fly due south. The airspeed of the plane is 185 MPH. There is a wind from the west at 40 MPH. What is the ground speed of the plane and in what direction should the pilot head?

3. A pilot wishes to fly due west. The airspeed of the plane is 195 MPH. There is a wind from the north at 45 MPH. In what direction should the pilot head? What is the groundspeed of the plane?

4. A pilot wishes to fly due south. There is a wind from 30° S of W (to 30° N of E) at 45 MPH. The airspeed of the plane is 200 MPH. What is the groundspeed and in what direction should the pilot head?

5. A pilot wishes to fly in a direction 35° N of E. There is a west wind (from the west) at 40 MPH. The airspeed of the plane is 200 MPH. What is the groundspeed and in what direction should the pilot head?

6. A pilot wishes to travel in a direction 40° N of W. There is a wind from the east at 35 MPH. The airspeed of the plane is 210 MPH. What is the groundspeed of the plane and in which direction should the pilot head?

7. A pilot wishes to travel due north. There is a wind from the north at 30 MPH. The airspeed of the plane is 185 MPH. What is the groundspeed of the plane and in which direction should the pilot head?

8. A pilot wishes to travel due north. There is a wind from the south at 30 MPH. The airspeed of the plane is 185 MPH. What is the groundspeed of the plane and in which direction should the pilot head?

9. A pilot wants to travel due west. The airspeed of the plane is 170 MPH. There is a wind from 34° N of W at 35 MPH. What is the groundspeed of the plane and in what direction should the pilot head?

10. A pilot wants to travel in a direction 32° N of E. The airspeed of the plane is 190 MPH. There is a wind from the west at 40 MPH. What is the groundspeed and what is the heading?

11. A pilot needs to travel due west. The airspeed is 190 MPH. There is a wind from the north at 38 MPH. What are the groundspeed and heading?

Chapter XVII

Applications of Bernoulli's Principle to Aircraft

Basic Definitions

Before we begin our discussion of the lift and drag on an airplane wing, the following definitions must be understood.

The relative wind direction is the direction of the airflow with respect to the wing and is opposite to the path of flight (figure 17-1).

The chord line of a wing is a straight line connecting the leading edge of a wing to its trailing edge (figure 17-2).

The angle of attack is the angle between the chord line of a wing and the relative wind direction (figure 17-3).

Figure 17-4 shows the cross section of a wing at rest and subject to atmospheric pressure which on the average is 14.7 lbs./in.^{2}

A force of 14.7 lbs. can be imagined as acting perpendicular to every square inch of the wing. The resultant of these 14.7 lbs. force vectors is zero and therefore has no effect on the dynamics of the plane.

It is the motion of air past the wing that alters the pressure pattern. Whether the wing is in motion through the air or the air is flowing past a stationary wing the result is the same.

For example, if a plane is moving through stationary air at a speed of 200 MPH, the effect is the same (as far as the plane and air are concerned) as if the plane were stationary and the air was moving with velocity 200 MPH past the plane.

As air streams past the wing of a plane, the speed of the air past the upper surface of the wing is greater than the speed of the air past the lower surface of the wing. These exact speeds are determined by the shape of the wing and the angle of attack.

For example, if the speed of the relative wind (equal to the speed of the plane) is 200 MPH, the speed of the air past the upper surface of the wind may be 210 MPH and the speed of air past the

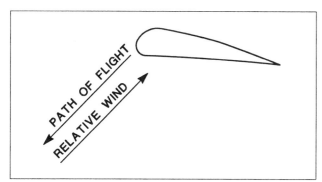

Figure 17-1.

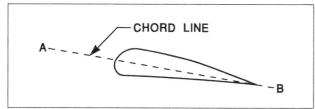

Figure 17-2.

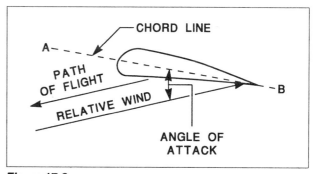

Figure 17-3.

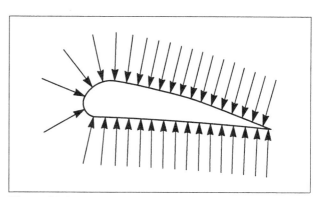

Figure 17-4.

lower surface of the wing may be 195 MPH. As indicated above, the exact values for a given case depend on the shape of the wing and the angle of attack.

In this example, we could say that the speed past the upper surface of the wing is [1.05 (200 MPH)] and the speed past the lower surface if the wing is [0.975 (200 MPH)].

In figure 17-5, the following symbols apply:

P_1 = pressure on the upper surface of the wing

P_2 = pressure on the lower surface of the wing

v_0 = relative wind velocity

ρ = density of the air

The speed past the upper surface of the wing is Av_0 and the speed past the lower wing surface is Bv_0.

We apply Bernoulli's principle (see figure 7-4):

$$P_1 + \frac{1}{2}\rho v_1^2 = P_2 + \frac{1}{2}\rho v_2^2$$

We note that the ones refer to the upper surface and the twos apply to the lower surface of the wing.

$$P_1 + \frac{1}{2}\rho (Av_0)^2 = P_2 + \frac{1}{2}\rho (Bv_0)^2$$

$$\frac{1}{2}\rho v_0^2 (A^2 - B^2) = P_2 - P_1$$

We note that $P_2 - P_1$ is the net upward pressure. If we multiply this net upward pressure by the wing area (S), we obtain the net upward force, the lift (L).

Also we introduce the coefficient of lift (C_L) as the value of $A_2 - B_2$. If we multiply by S, we have:

$$(\frac{1}{2}\rho v_0^2) C_L S = (P_2 - P_1) S$$

We also define the dynamic pressure of the air stream (q).

$$q = \frac{1}{2}\rho v_0^2 = \text{dynamic pressure of the air stream}$$

Finally, we have the important equation:

$$q S C_L = L$$

We usually switch the members of this equation and write:

$$L = qSC_L$$

It should be noted that when we use the term "wing area", we mean both wings and only the upper (or lower) surface of these two wings.

In an analogous manner we define the drag as:

$$D = qSC_D$$

where C_D is the coefficient of drag.

The lift coefficient and the values of the quantities A and B depend on the wing shape and the angle of attack.

EXAMPLE 17-A.

Suppose that the relative wind that a wing experiences is 200 MPH (293 ft./sec.). The air speed past the upper surface of the wing is 220 MPH (322 ft./sec.) and past the lower surface is 198 MPH (290 ft./sec.). The density of the air is 0.002377 slug/ft.^{3} The wing area is 400 ft. Calculate the lift.

$$q = \frac{1}{2}\rho v_0^2$$

$$q = \frac{1}{2}(0.002377 \text{ slug/ft.}^3)(293 \frac{\text{ft.}}{\text{sec.}})^2$$

$$q = 102 \frac{\text{lbs.}}{\text{ft.}^2}$$

Note that q is the dynamic pressure and has the dimensions of a pressure.

$$A = \frac{322}{293} = 1.10 \qquad \text{and} \qquad B = \frac{290}{293} = 0.99$$

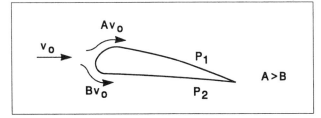

Figure 17-5.

$$C_L = A^2 - B^2 = (1.10)^2 - (0.99)^2$$

$$C_L = 0.23$$

$$L = qSC_L$$

$$L = (102 \text{ lbs./ft.}^2)(400 \text{ ft.}^2)(0.23)$$

$$L = 9,380 \text{ lbs.}$$

Cruising Flight

When a plane is cruising (flying in a straight line at constant speed and constant altitude) the upward force on the plane, the lift, must equal the weight of the plane. Also the thrust is equal to the drag.

Aerodynamic Characteristics of an Airfoil

The lift coefficient (C_L) and the drag coefficient (C_D) are usually determined, not by measuring the speed of the air past the upper and lower surfaces of the wing, but rather by measuring the lift and drag forces in a wind tunnel. A particular wing, having a definite shape, is placed in a wind tunnel. The angle of attack is then varied and the lift and drag are determined for each angle of attack. A graph is drawn. There is a sample of such a graph on the next page. The data are for the aerodynamic characteristics of an NACA 23045 airfoil.

In using such a graph, it is important to determine from the given problem the angle of attack and to find the lift and drag coefficients from the curves on the graph.

We note that each type of airfoil has its own characteristic graph drawn as the result of much experimentation in a wind tunnel.

The graph in figure 17-6 is taken from Technical Report 669, a publication of the National Advisory Committee for Aeronautics (NACA) and the Aeronautical Research Council (ARC).

Airfoil Section Data Obtained in the NACA Variable-Density Tunnel As Affected by Support Interference and Other Corrections, by Eastman N. Jacobs and Ira H. Abbott, 1939.

The following example and problems refer to a NACA 23045 airfoil having an aspect ratio of 6. See figure 17-6 for the graph.

EXAMPLE 17-B.

A plane having wing area 600 ft.2 is flying at an altitude of 10,000 ft. and with an angle of attack of 6É. The speed of the plane is 286 MPH. What is the lift?

At 10,000 ft., the air density is 0.001756 slug/ft.^{3}

$$v_0 = 286 \text{ MPH} = 419 \text{ ft./sec.}$$

$$q = \frac{1}{2}\rho\, v_0{}^2$$

$$q = \frac{1}{2}(0.001756 \text{ slug/ft.}^3)(419 \text{ ft./sec.})^2$$

$$q = 154 \text{ lbs./ft.}^2$$

$$C_L = 0.54 \text{ (from the graph)}$$

$$L = qSC_L$$

$$L = (154 \frac{\text{lbs.}}{\text{ft.}^2})(600 \text{ ft.}^2)(0.54)$$

$$L = 50,000 \text{ lbs.}$$

Turning Flight

In our discussion of cruising flight, the forces acting on the plane cancelled and the acceleration was zero. In turning flight, there is acceleration (the plane is constantly changing direction) and Newton's second law provides the necessary link between this acceleration and the forces required to bring it about.

Figure 17-7 is a Mitsubishi Marquis turboprop powered business transport in a level turn. In order to maintain level flight, the component of lift in the verical direction must just balance the weight. We denote the angle of bank by the Greek letter theta (θ).

The sum of the forces in vertical direction must be zero. This gives us the equation:

$$(1) \qquad w = mg = L \cos\theta$$

Also, we know that the horizontal component of the lift ($L \sin\theta$), gives the centripetal force which keeps the plane in its circular path. This centripetal force equals the mass of the plane times its centripetal acceleration. We recall that the centrip-

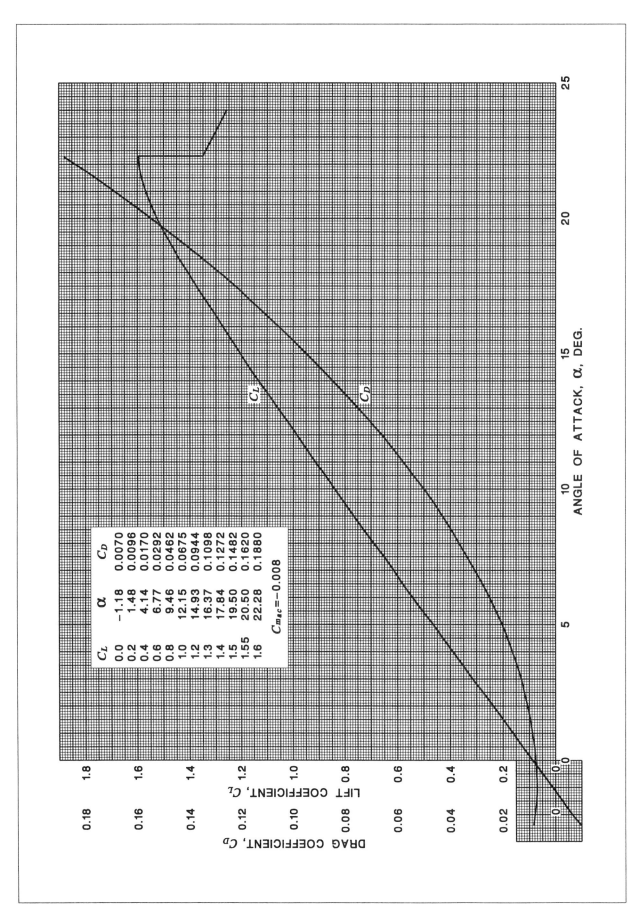

C_L	α	C_D
0.0	−1.18	0.0070
0.2	1.48	0.0096
0.4	4.14	0.0170
0.6	6.77	0.0292
0.8	9.46	0.0462
1.0	12.15	0.0675
1.2	14.93	0.0944
1.3	16.37	0.1098
1.4	17.84	0.1272
1.5	19.50	0.1482
1.55	20.50	0.1620
1.6	22.28	0.1880

$C_{mac} = -0.008$

Figure 17-6.

122

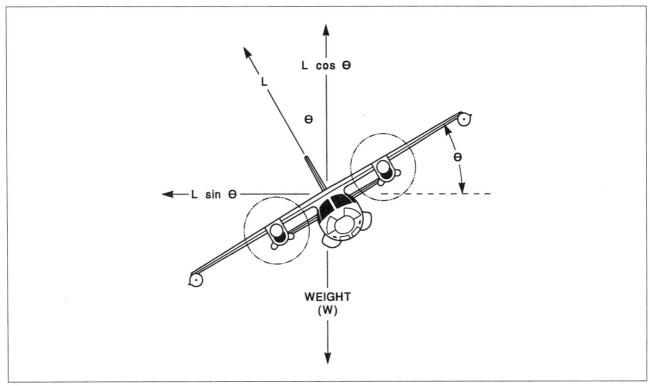

Figure 17-7.

etal acceleration equals the square of speed of the plane divided by the radius of the turn.

$$(2) \qquad \frac{mv^2}{R} = L \sin \theta$$

Since both equations involve m, L, and the angle (θ), a new equation can be obtained by dividing equation (2) by equation (1) and noting that some quantities cancel out.

$$\frac{L \sin \theta}{L \cos \theta} = \frac{m v^2 / R}{m g}$$

There is a trigonometric identity that tells us that:

$$\tan \theta = \frac{\sin \theta}{\cos \theta}$$

We also note that L and m cancel. We obtain the form:

$$\tan \theta = \frac{v^2}{R g}$$

This equation can be rewritten in the form:

$$(3) \qquad v^2 = R g \tan \theta$$

Let us return to equation (2).

$$L \sin \theta = \frac{mv^2}{R}$$

$$L = \frac{mv^2}{R \sin \theta}$$

Also:

$$L = qSC_L = (\tfrac{1}{2} \rho v^2)SC_L$$

Therefore:

$$\tfrac{1}{2} \rho v^2 S C_L = v^2 \frac{m}{R \sin \theta}$$

We cancel the v^2 and obtain:

$$\tfrac{1}{2} \rho S C_L = \frac{m}{R \sin \theta}$$

$$(4) \qquad R = \frac{2m}{\rho\, C_L\, S\, \sin\theta}$$

Equations (3) and (4) are important equations for the following problems.

EXAMPLE 17-C.

A DC-9 cruising at 10,000 meters at a speed of 821 km/hr. weighs 530,000 N and has a wing area of 93 m^2. Determine the lift coefficient under these conditions. Assuming the same lift coefficient, find the radius of the a turn executed with a 15° banking angle. Find the speed needed to maintain a level turn at a 15° banking angle.

$$v_0 = 821 \text{ km/hr.} = 228 \text{ m/sec.}$$

At 10,000 m,

$$\rho = 0.414 \text{ kg/m}^3$$

$$w = 530,000 \text{ N}$$

$$m = w/g = 54,100 \text{ kg}$$

$$S = 93 \text{ m}^2$$

The lift (L) = the weight, (w)

$$L = qSC_L = w$$

$$C_L = \frac{w}{q\,s} \qquad q = \frac{1}{2}\rho\, v_0{}^2$$

$$C_L = \frac{530,000 \text{ N}}{[(0.5)\,(0.414 \text{ kg/m}^3)\,(228 \text{ m/sec.})^2]\,(93 \text{ m}^2)}$$

$$C_L = 0.530$$

$$R = \frac{2m}{\rho\, C_L\, S\, \sin\theta}$$

$$R = \frac{2(54\,100 \text{ kg})}{(0.414 \text{ kg/m}^3)\,(0.530)\,(93 \text{ m}^2)\,\sin 15°}$$

$$R = 20,500 \text{ m}$$

$$v^2 = R\,g\,\tan\theta = (20,500 \text{ m})\,(9.8 \text{ m/sec.}^2)\,\tan 15°$$

$$v = 232 \text{ m/sec.} = 835 \text{ km/hr.}$$

Let us return to the equation for the radius of turning flight:

$$R = \frac{2\,w/g}{\rho\, C_L\, S\, \sin\theta}$$

What do we learn from this equation?
1. A larger radius is required for low values of the coefficient of lift. Thus for low angles of attack the radius will be larger than for greater angles of attack.
2. The radius required to maintain a turn increases with altitude since the density of the air decreases with altitude.
3. The heavier the plane, the greater the radius of turn required.
4. The smaller the angle of bank (θ) the larger the radius of the turn.

Chapter XVII Problems

The following problems deal with cruising flight.

1. A plane having wing area 500 ft.^{2} is moving at 250 MPH. The speed of the air moving past the top surface of the wing is 290 MPH and the speed of the air past the bottom surface of the wing is 230 MPH. The density of the air is 0.002378 slug/ft.^{3} What is the lift?

2. A plane having wing area 460 ft.^{2} is cruising at 240 MPH. The speed of the air moving past the top surface of the wing is 265 MPH and the speed of the air past the bottom surface of the wing is 235 MPH. The density of the air is 0.002365 slug/ft.^{3} What is the weight of the plane?

3. A plane is cruising at 310 MPH. The speed of the air moving past the top surface of the wing is 335 MPH and the speed of the air past the bottom surface of the wing is 299 MPH. The density of the air is 0.002377 slug/ft.^{3} The weight of the plane is 26,600 lbs. What is the wing area?

4. A Beechcraft Duke B60 has a maximum cruising speed at 25,000 feet of 239 knots. Find the dynamic pressure. Determine the lift coefficient if the weight is 6,775 lbs. and the wing area is 213 ft.^{2}

5. A Boeing 727 has a stalling speed at sea level with flaps down of 193 km/hr. The weight of the 727 is 712,000 N and its wing area is 157.9 m^2.

Determine the dynamic pressure. Determine the lift coefficient.

6. A Cessna Citation I has a stalling apeed at sea level of 82 knots at a maximum landing weight of 50,500 N. Its wing area is 25.9 m^2. Determine the lift coefficient.

7. A plane having wing area 500 ft.^{2} is flying at 310 MPH with an angle of attack of 7°. The altitude is 5,000 ft. What is the lift?

8. A plane is flying at 8,000 ft. altitude. The wing area is 450 ft.^{2} The angle of attack is 8°. At what speed will the lift on this plane be 40,000 lbs.?

9. A Cessna Titan has a cruising speed at 20,000 ft. of 175 knots, with a weight of 9,660 lbs. and a wing area of 242 ft.^{2} Determine the lift coefficient under these conditions. Maintaining the same lift coefficient, what is the radius of a level turn executed at a 37° banking angle? What speed is required to execute this turn?

10. A Piper Seneca cruising at 170 knots at an altitude of 15,000 ft. has a weight of 4,800 lbs. and a wing area of 209 ft.^{2} Determine the lift coefficient under these conditions. Maintaining the same lift coefficient, what is the radius of a level turn executed at 30° banking angle? Find the speed needed to maintain this level turn.

Chapter XVIII

Newton's Law of Gravitation

In chapter 6, we discussed the three laws of motion known as Newton's Laws. There is a fourth law which was formulated by Isaac Newton in the middle of the seventeenth century. This law is known as the law of gravitation and explains many common phenomena. Note that this law describes for us in clear mathematical language a basic law of nature. This law tells us "how nature operates".

In words we say that all bodies in the universe attract each other with a force which varies directly with the product of the masses of the bodies and inversely with the square of the distance, between the bodies. This distance is measured from the center of one body to the center of the other.

In symbols, we write the equation:

$$F = G \frac{m_1 m_2}{r^2}$$

In this equation:

F is the force of attraction measured in Newtons.

m_1 and m_2 are the masses of the two bodies measured in kilograms.

r is the distance between the centers of the two bodies measured in meters.

G is called the gravitational constant. It is a well known physical constant and has a numerical value and a unit.

In our calculations, we will use the accepted value for G, i.e.,

$$G = 6.67 \times 10^{-11} \frac{Nm^2}{kg^2}$$

EXAMPLE 18-A.

Suppose that two bodies of masses 20 kg and 50 kg are exactly 5 meters apart measured from their centers. Calculate the force in Newtons with which the two bodies attract each other.

We substitute in the equation for Newton's law of gravitation. Also note that we can cancel units.

$$F = 6.67 \times 10^{-11} \frac{Nm^2}{kg^2} \frac{(20 \text{ kg}) (50 \text{ kg})}{(5 \text{ meters})^2}$$

$$F = 267 \times 10^{-11} \text{ N}$$

Usually we rewrite our answer in the form where there is just one significant digit before the decimal point.

$$F = 2.67 \times 10^{-9} \text{ N}$$

Note that in the second-to-last equation we are instructed to move the decimal point 11 places to the left while in the last equation we are to move the decimal point 9 places to the left. In either case we arrive as the same number, 0.00000000267 N. Of course, we do express our answer in scientific notation because it is less confusing.

This force is very tiny as you can well imagine. However, when we deal with astronomical bodies, gravitational forces of attraction are very important. It is this force of attraction which keeps astronomical bodies in their precise orbits.

In chapter 5 we discussed centripetal acceleration and in chapter 6 we discussed centripetal force. You recall that, in the case of a body moving in a circular path, Newton's second law, F = ma, has the form:

$$F = \frac{mv^2}{R}$$

In this equation, F is the centripetal force (force directed toward the center of the circle), m is the mass of the body in kilograms, v is the speed of the body in meters/second, and R is the radius of the circle in meters. The force needed to keep a body moving in a circular path is expressed in Newtons.

If the body is a stone attached to a string and whirled by an instructor in a physics class, the centripetal force is applied by the instructor as he pulls on the string and causes the stone to move in a circle (figure 18-1).

If the body is the moon as it moves in a circular path about the earth, the centripetal force is the gravitational attraction that the earth exerts on the moon (figure 18-2).

We will use Newton's law of gravitation to calculate this force:

$$F = G\frac{m_1m_2}{R^2}$$

See the Table of Astronomical Data (figure 18-3).

$$F =$$
$$6.67 \times 10^{-11}\frac{Nm^2}{kg^2}\frac{(5.99 \times 10^{24}kg)\,(7.36 \times 10^{22}kg)}{(3.84 \times 10^8m)^2}$$

$$F = 19.9 \times 10^{19}N \times \frac{0.2248\;lb.}{1\;N} = 4.48 \times 10^{19}\;lbs.$$

The moon experiences this enormous force which keeps pulling the moon into its circular path

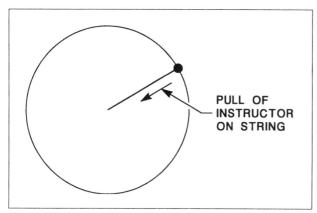

Figure 18-1.

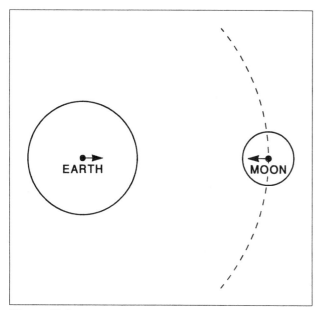

Figure 18-2.

about the earth just as your instructor keeps pulling a stone into a circular path as he whirls it in a circle in your classroom.

There is a relationship between g (the acceleration of a freely falling body) and G (the gravitational constant). In figure 18-4, we show a body of mass (m) at or close to the surface of the earth. We note that "close to" means that the distance of the body above the surface of the earth is negligible relative to the radius of the earth.

In figure 18-4 we use the notation:

$$M_E = \text{mass of the earth}$$
$$R_E = \text{average radius of the earth}$$
$$m = \text{mass of a body at or close to the surface of the earth}$$

Newton's law of gravitation tells us that the force with which the earth pulls on mass (m) is:

$$F = G\frac{m\,M_E}{R_E{}^2}$$

However, we also know that this force is, by definition, the weight of a body (mg). Therefore, we can equate the weight (mg) to the right member of the equation above.

Therefore, we have:

$$mg = G\frac{m\,M_E}{R_E{}^2}$$

PHYSICAL AND ASTRONIMICAL DATA	
Acceleration Due to Gravity, g	$9.80\ m/sec.^2$
Average Earth-Moon Distance	$3.84 \times 10^8 m$
Average Earth-Sun Distance	$1.49 \times 10^{11} m$
Average Radius of the Earth	$6.37 \times 10^6\ m$
Mass of the Earth	$5.99 \times 10^{24} kg$
Mass of the Moon	$7.36 \times 10^{22} kg$
Mass of the Sun	$1.99 \times 10^{30} kg$
Gravitational Constant, G	$6.67 \times 10^{-11}\dfrac{Nm^2}{kg^2}$

Figure 18-3.

We note that the mass (m) cancels giving us:

$$g = G \frac{M_E}{R_E^2}$$

Therefore, the equation relating g to G can be written:

$$g R_E^2 = G M_E$$

Substitute the values from figure 18-3 to verify that this equation makes sense!

We recall that the acceleration due to gravity,

$$g = 9.80 \text{ m/sec.}^2 = 32 \text{ ft./sec.}^2$$

is the rate at which any body of any mass accelerates as it falls to the earth at a distance close to the surface of the earth. In the preceding sentence, the words "close to" mean that the distance of the falling body from the surface of the earth is negligible relative to the radius of the earth. The radius of the earth can be expressed in various units. On the table, we see that this radius is 6,370,000 meters. Using conversion factors we can also say that:

$$R_E = 6,370 \text{ km} = 3,960 \text{ mi.} = 20,000,000 \text{ ft.}$$

Therefore, if a body falls to the surface of the earth from a distance of, say, 5,000 ft. (approximately one mile) this distance is still negligible relative to the radius of the earth and the body would still accelerate at a rate of 32 ft./sec.^{2}

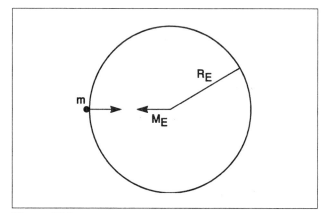

Figure 18-4.

Earth Satellites

Newton's law of gravitation enables us to understand the motion of man-made earth satellites. We note that the moon is also an earth satellite but it is not man-made.

In our discussion below, we will use the symbol m for the mass of the satellite, r for the radius of the path of the satellite, and v for the speed of the satellite in its path.

The gravitational attraction supplies the force which keeps the satellite moving in its circular path about the earth. Thus, we can equate the gravitational force to the centripetal force.

$$\frac{G m M_E}{r^2} = \frac{mv^2}{r}$$

We note that the mass of the satellite (m) drops out of this equation and that one of the r's cancels also. We are left with the equation:

$$\frac{G M_E}{r} = v^2$$

We can also write this equation:

$$r v^2 = G M_E$$

We note that for a satellite of any mass the product of the radius of the path and the square of the speed remains constant. This constant is the product of the constant G and the constant mass of the earth.

Usually, when we are discussng satellites and the radii of their orbits we use the term altitude, the distance of the satellite above the surface of the earth. We recall that the radius of the earth in large metric units is 6,370 km. Therefore if the altitude of an earth satelllite is 3,000 km, the radius of the orbit of the satellite (r) in the above equation is 9,370 km.

Let us calculate the speed in m/sec. of an earth satellite if it is circulating the earth at an altitude of 3,000 km.

We use the equation:

$$r v^2 = G M_E$$

We note that in this case:

$$r = 9,370 \text{ km} = 9,370,000 \text{ m} = 9.37 \times 10^6 \text{ m}$$

Therefore:

$$(9.37 \times 10^6 \text{ m}) \, v^2 =$$

$$(6.67 \times 10^{-11} \frac{N \, m^2}{kg^2}) \, (5.99 \times 10^{24} \text{ kg})$$

$$v^2 = 4.26 \times 10^7 \frac{m^2}{s^2}$$

We now take the square root of both members of this equation.

$$v = 6.53 \times 10^3 \frac{m}{s}$$

We can also find the period (T) for this satellite. The period is defined as the time for the satellite to complete one complete motion of its orbit. It follows that one circumference equals the speed (v) times the period (T).

Therefore, the period is the circumference of the orbit divided by the velocity of the satellite in its orbit. We can write the equation:

$$T = \frac{2 \pi r}{v}$$

We now substitute the values:

$$T = \frac{2 \, (3.1416) \, (9.37 \times 10^6)}{(6.53 \times 10^3)}$$

$$T = 9.02 \times 10^3 \text{ sec.} = 9,020 \text{ sec.}$$
$$= 150 \text{ min.} = 2.5 \text{ hr.}$$

We have learned a great deal about a satellite launched from earth to an altitude of 3,000 km.

Its speed in its orbit is $6.53 \times 10^3 \frac{m}{s}$.
The radius of the orbit is 9.37×10^6 m.
The time for a complete orbiting of the earth is 2.5 hr.

Satellites In Geosynchronous Orbits

A satellite in a "geosynchronous" orbit is one which is launched at such an altitude that its period is 24 hours (8.64×10^4 sec.). Such a period has an advantage for "spy satellites". A satellite in a geosynchronous orbit remains above the same place on the earth's surface at all times in its motion. It is thus able to continuously obtain data regarding what is occurring at a certain place on earth!

Two different equations are needed to obtain the necessary launching altitude for a geosynchronous satellite. These equations are two equations from this chapter:

$$r v^2 = G M_E \quad \text{and} \quad T = \frac{2 \pi r}{v}$$

Let us square the second of these two equations:

$$T^2 = \frac{4 \pi^2 r^2}{v^2}$$

Next we multiply numerator and denominator of the right member of this equation by r.

$$T^2 = \frac{4 \pi^2 r^3}{r v^2}$$

Now we can substitute $G M_E$ in the denominator of this equation.

Finally, we obtain the equation we need:

$$T^2 = \frac{4 \pi^2 r^3}{G M_E}$$

Solving this equation for the cube of the radius of the orbit we have:

$$r^3 = \frac{T^2 G M_E}{4 \pi^2}$$

We now substitute our known values:

$$r^3 = \frac{(8.64 \times 10^4)^2 \, (6.67 \times 10^{-11}) \, (5.99 \, 10^{24})}{4(3.1416)^2}$$

$$r^3 = 75.5 \times 10^{21} \text{ m}^3$$

Now we must take the cube root of each member of the equation. We obtain:

$$r = 4.23 \times 10^7 \text{ m} = 42.3 \times 10^6 \text{m}$$

Note that this number is the radius of the orbit. We must still subtract the radius of the earth to obtain the required altitude.

$$\text{Altitude} = 42.3 \times 10^6 m - 6.4 \times 10^6 m$$
$$= 35.9 \times 10^6 m$$

We can change this altitude to miles.

$$\text{Altitude} = 35.9 \times 10^6 m \times \frac{1 \text{ mile}}{1,609 \text{ m}}$$
$$= 22,300 \text{ miles}$$

We can now understand the problem with "spy" satellites. A satellite in a geosynchronous orbit stays above the same place on the earth's surface at all times. However, it has to be so far above the earth's surface that **very powerful** optical equipment must be provided so that the satellite's "eye" can see anything!

Because of the problem discussed above, most "spy" satellites are in low earth orbits because the power of surveilance equipment has to be so great for geosynchronous orbits. Of course for low earth orbits the surveilance isn't continuous. U.S. "spy" satellites are launched from the West Coast into a more North-South orbit to cover the whole earth on a more regular basis than they would get from a Florida launch which is more East-West.

Satellites used as television relays use geosynchronous orbits so that the "dish" antennae on earth can be kept fixed on one point and don't have to "track" the satellite.

Intelstat, a telecommunication satellite, was launched by a consortium with 122 member nations. This 157 million dollar satellite was left in a uselessly low orbit by a mis-wired Titan rocket. In May, 1992, spacewalking Endeavor astronauts plucked the satellite from space and attached a motor to boost it to its proper geosynchronous orbit, 22,300 miles high. This operation was shown on national TV.

The National Weather Service also uses satellite in geosynchronous orbits to obtain weather information. These weather satellites stay in fixed orbits above the United States.

Weightlessness

We experience "weight" when we feel the floor (or the seat of our chair or bed) pushing up on our bodies. This is our psychological experience of weight. If we do not experience such a feeling of an upward push or force, we say that we feel "weightless". Note that the word is put in quotation marks since we are never really weightless, since the earth is always pulling on us. However, there are several times that we, at the surface of the earth, feel "weightless". One example of "weightlessness" occurs when we jump off a diving board. As we are descending to the water, we feel "weightless" since there is no upward push on us during this brief period of time.

Whenever a person is in a "freely-falling" state, he experiences the condition known as "weightlessness". Circus performers, daredevils, people who jump from burning buildings to a safety net below all have experienced "weightlessness". It is important to realize that in all of these cases these people do have weight (the earth is pulling on them). However, they do not feel, during the seconds they are falling, the upward push of the earth's surface on their bodies. Hence, during these brief seconds, they feel "weightless".

When an astronaut is in a spacecraft he is a mini-satellite himself. He is a body circling the earth in such a way that the equation $r v^2 = G M_E$ applies to him as well as to the whole spacecraft. The earth is exerting a force on him of just the right amount to keep him moving about the earth in a circular orbit of radius (r) and speed (v). When we see pictures of astronauts sent to us from an orbiting spacecraft we see the astronauts "floating" about the cabin. They are not "sitting" or "standing" or experiencing an upward push of a chair seat or a floor on their bodies. They feel "weightless". Try to observe this "floating" condition the next time you see pictures sent to earth from an orbiting spacecraft.

Chapter XVIII Problems

1. What is the magnitude (in Newtons) of the gravitational attraction between the sun and the earth? Look up the needed constants in the table of physical and astronomical data.

2. A spacecraft is in circular orbit about the earth at an altitude of 500 km. What is the orbital speed of this spacecraft? Be sure to obtain the correct radius of the orbit by adding the altitude to the radius of the earth.

3. What is the period of the spacecraft as described in the preceding problem?

4. At what altitude will a spacecraft have a period of 6 hours? Hint: Recall the calculation that was necessary to determine the altitude of a spacecraft having a period of 24 hours. Do the same type of calculation.

5. At what altitude will a spacecraft in a circular orbit have a speed of 15,000 MPH?

6. The Space Shuttle was launched at an altitude of 400 km. Calculate its speed in m/sec. and its period in hours.

Chapter XIX

Momentum and Collision Problems

Definition of Momentum

Momentum is a vector quantity (**p**) defined as the product of mass times velocity. Note that velocity (**v**) is also a vector quantity. We write the defining equation as:

$$\mathbf{p} = m\mathbf{v}$$

Momentum is a very important quantity when we are dealing with collisions, because it is conserved in all such cases.

Conservation of Momentum

In a collision, there are always at least two bodies that collide. We will deal only with collisions of two bodies. We will also limit our discussion to collisions occurring in one dimension. Such collisions are called "head-on" collisions.

At this time, we need to recall two of Newton's laws. We need Newton's second law, $F = ma$, and Newton's third law, which tells us that if two bodies collide, the force that the first body exerts on the second body is equal in magnitude and opposite in direction to the force that the second body exerts on the first body. Also recall that the acceleration (a) equals the change in the velocity (symbolized by the Greek letter Delta, Δ) divided by the time (t).

Now let us visualize two bodies of masses, m_1 and m_2, on a one dimensional track.

If these two bodies collide, we have four different velocities to consider. We will name these velocities very carefully.

v_1' = the velocity of body one before the collision

v_1'' = the velocity of body one after the collision

v_2' = the velocity of body two before the collision

v_2'' = the velocity of body two after the collision

From Newton's two laws, we can conclude that:

$$m_1 \frac{\Delta v_1}{t} = -m_2 \frac{\Delta v_2}{t}$$

After cancelling the times, we obtain:

$$m_1(v_1'' - v_1') = -m_2(v_2'' - v_2')$$

If we remove the parentheses, transpose terms, and switch left and right members we obtain:

$$m_1 v_1' + m_2 v_2' = m_1 v_1'' + m_2 v_2''$$

The equation tells us that the total momentum before the collision is equal to the total momentum after the collision. Sometimes we say simply that "momentum is conserved".

Recoil Problems

The simplest example of the conservation of momentum is in recoil problems.

EXAMPLE 19-A.

A boy and a man are both on ice skates on a pond. The mass of the boy is 20 kg and the mass of the man is 80 kg. They push on each other and move in opposite directions. If the recoil velocity of the boy is 80 m/sec., what is the recoil velocity of the man?

First we note that both the man and the boy are at rest before the collision occurs.

$$m_1 v_1' + m_2 v_2' = m_1 v_1'' + m_2 v_2''$$

$$(20)(0) + (80)(0) = (20)(80) + (80)v_2''$$

$$0 = 1,600 + 80v_2''$$

$$-1,600 = 80 v_2''$$

$$v_2'' = -20 \text{ m/sec.}$$

The negative sign indicates that the man recoils in the opposite direction from the boy.

Collision Problems

Whenever two bodies collide, momentum is always conserved. This is simply the result of applying Newton's second and third laws as we have done in the preceding discussion.

Sometimes kinetic energy is also conserved in a collision. This happens when the bodies are so hard that there is very little deformation of the bodies in the actual collision process. Billiard balls are a good example. These collisions are know as elastic collisions. We will derive a formula for determining the velocities of the bodies after the collision has occurred.

Another type of collision that we will discuss is the perfectly inelastic collision. In this type of collision, the bodies are deformed so much that they actually stick together after the collision. An example would be the collision of two masses of putty. We will also do some problems for this type of collision.

Of course, there are collisions which are neither elastic nor inelastic. We will leave the discussion of these collisions to your next physics course.

Inelastic Collisions

We use the conservation of momentum for dealing with this type of collision. As we have said, the colliding bodies stick together after impact. Therefore, the equation is simply:

$$m_1 v_1' + m_2 v_2' = (m_1 + m_2) v''$$

Note that we use the symbol v'' for the common velocity of the two bodies (which are now one body) after the collision.

It is important to include the signs of the velocities of the bodies in setting up momentum equations. As usual, we use a positive sign for east and a negative sign for west, a positive sign for north and a negative sign for south.

EXAMPLE 19-B.

A truck of mass 1,550 kg is moving east at 60 m/sec. A car of mass 1,250 kg is traveling west at 90 m/sec. The vehicles collide and stick together after impact. What is the velocity of the combined mass after the collision has occurred?

$$v_1' = 60 \text{ m/sec.}$$

$$m_1 = 1,550 \text{ kg}$$

$$v_2' = -90 \text{ m/sec.}$$

$$m_2 = 1,250 \text{ kg}$$

$$m_1 v_1 + m_2 v_2 = (m_1 + m_2) v''$$

We will not include units in our substitution. However, we will note that the velocity, when we obtain it, will be in m/sec.

$$(1,550)(60) + (1,250)(-90) = (1,550 + 1,250)v''$$

$$-19,500 = 2,800 \, v''$$

$$v'' = -6.96 \text{ m/sec.}$$

Since the calculated velocity has a negative sign, we conclude that the combined mass is traveling west after the impact has occurred.

Our answer is that the wreckage starts moving west with a speed of 6.96 m/sec.

===

Sometimes the principle of conservation of momentum in the case of an inelastic collision can be used by the police to determine the speed of a vehicle engaged in a head-on collision.

Suppose that a large truck with a weight of 12,000 lbs. (mass of 375 slugs) traveling east with an unknown velocity enters into a head-on collision with a smaller truck of weight 6,400 lbs. (mass of 200 slugs) initially traveling west with a speed of 30 MPH (44 ft./sec.). The trucks stick together in the collision and marks on the highway indicate that the wreckage traveled a distance of 120 feet east. The condition of the roadway (amount of friction) indicates that the wreckage would travel for a time of 4 sec. Determine the initial speed of the large truck.

The equation:

$$S = \left(\frac{v_f + v_i}{2}\right) t$$

can be used to determine the initial velocity of the wreckage. Note that the final velocity of the wreckage is zero.

$$v_i = \frac{2S}{t} = \frac{2(120 \text{ ft.})}{4 \text{ sec.}} = 60 \text{ ft./sec.}$$

Next, we can use the conservation of momentum equation to determine the velocity of the large truck at the instant of the impact. We will use the symbol V to represent this velocity.

$$(375 \text{ slugs}) (V) + (200 \text{ slugs}) (-44 \text{ ft./sec.})$$
$$= (575 \text{ slugs}) (60 \text{ ft./sec.})$$

$$375\,V = 43,300$$

$$V = 115 \text{ ft./sec.}$$

$$V = 78.4 \text{ MPH}$$

Elastic Collisions

Elastic collisions are collisions that occur between bodies that deform very little in the collision. Therefore we assume that no energy is lost. An example of such a collision is the collision between pool balls.

In elastic collisions, both kinetic energy and momentum are conserved. In an ordinary elastic collision problem, we know the masses and the velocities of two bodies that will collide. We want to predict, by a mathematical calculation, the velocities the bodies will have after the collision has occurred, the two unknowns. If we write the two conservation equations, we have two equations in these two unknowns. It is possible to solve these two equations for these two unknowns. However, one of the conservation equations, the energy equation, is a "second order" equation. A "second order" equation contains the squares of the unknowns. This makes the solution more difficult. Instead, we will use an algebraic trick! The two conservation equations can be solved together producing a third equation. This third equation and the momentum conservation equation provide the two first order equations that we will use in solving elastic collision problems.

We will write the two conservation equations:

Conservation of Energy

(1)
$$\frac{1}{2} m_1 v_1'^2 + \frac{1}{2} m_2 v_2'^2$$
$$= \frac{1}{2} m_1 v_1''^2 + \frac{1}{2} m_2 v_2''^2$$

Conservation of Momentum

(2)
$$m_1 v_1' + m_2 v_2' = m_1 v_1'' + m_2 v_2''$$

Divide (1) by ½:

(3)
$$m_1 v_1'^2 + m_2 v_2'^2$$
$$= m_1 v_1''^2 + m_2 v_2''^2$$

Now in both (2) and (3), we will transpose some terms:

(4)
$$m_1 v_1' - m_1 v_1'' = m_2 v_2'' - m_2 v_2'$$

(5)
$$m_1 v_1'^2 - m_1 v_1''^2$$
$$= m_2 v_2''^2 - m_2 v_2'^2$$

Factor (4) and (5):

(6)
$$m_1(v_1' - v_1'') = m_2(v_2'' - v_2')$$

(7)
$$m_1(v_1'^2 - v_1''^2)$$
$$= m_2(v_2''^2 - v_2'^2)$$

In (7), factor again:

(8)
$$m_1(v_1' - v_1'')(v_1' + v_1'')$$
$$= m_2(v_2'' - v_2')(v_2'' + v_2')$$

Divide (8) by (6):

$$\frac{\cancel{m_1}(\cancel{v_1' - v_1''})(v_1' + v_1'')}{\cancel{m_1}(\cancel{v_1' - v_1''})}$$
$$= \frac{\cancel{m_2}(\cancel{v_2'' - v_2'})(v_2'' + v_2')}{\cancel{m_2}(\cancel{v_2'' - v_2'})}$$

After cancelling common factors, we obtain:

$$v_1' + v_1'' = v_2'' + v_2'$$

Again we transpose terms:

(9)
$$v_1' - v_2' = v_2'' - v_1''$$

In words, this equation says that the relative velocity of the balls before the collision is equal to the relative velocity of the balls after the collision.

Equation (9) has been obtained algebraically from two equations, the conservation of momentum and the conservation of energy. We use equations (2), the conservation of momentum equation, and equation (9), called the relative velocity equation, to solve for the velocities of the two bodies after an elastic collision.

We will rewrite these two important equations for future reference:

$$(2) \qquad m_1 v_1' + m_2 v_2' = m_1 v_1'' + m_2 v_2''$$

$$(9) \qquad v_1' - v_2' = v_2'' - v_1''$$

In using these two equations, the two unknowns are usually v_1'' and v_2'', the velocities of the two bodies after the collision has occurred. The known quantities are usually the two masses and the velocities of the bodies before the collision. Also be careful to include the signs of the velocities. If you forget to do this, you will always end up with incorrect results.

EXAMPLE 19-C.

A billiard ball of mass 2 kg is moving east at 3 m/sec. and undergoes an elastic collision with another billiard ball of mass 3 kg moving west at 4 m/sec. Find the velocities of the two balls after the collision.

$$m_1 = 2 \qquad\qquad v_1' = 3 \text{ (east)}$$
$$m_2 = 3 \qquad\qquad v_2' = -4 \text{ (west)}$$

Substitute in equation (2):

$$(2)(3) + (3)(-4) = 2 v_1'' + 3 v_2''$$

$$(10) \qquad\qquad -6 = 2v_1'' + 3v_2''$$

Substitute in equation (9):

$$3 - (-4) = v_2'' - v_1''$$

$$(11) \qquad\qquad 7 = v_2'' - v_1''$$

Rewrite equations (10) and (11) putting the unknowns in the left members and in order.

$$(10) \qquad 2 v_1'' + 3 v_2'' = -6$$

$$(11) \qquad -v_1'' + v_2'' = 7$$

We now have two equations in two unknowns. There are several methods of solving such a system of equations. We will use the method of addition. In this method we multiply either or both of the equations by constants to make the coefficient of one of the unknowns in one of the equations a positive number and to make the coefficient of this same unknown in the other equation a negative number of the same magnitude. We then add the two equations to eliminate one of the unknowns. We then solve for the other unknown by substituting in either equation.

We will multiply (11) by the number 2.

$$(12) \qquad -2 v_1'' + 2 v_2'' = 14$$

Add (10) and (12):

$$5 v_2'' = 8$$

$$v_2'' = 1.6 \text{ m/sec.}$$

Substitute this value back into (11):

$$-v_1'' + 1.6 = 7$$

$$-v_1'' = 7 - 1.6$$

$$-v_1'' = 5.4$$

$$v_1'' = -5.4 \text{ m/sec.}$$

We note that we interpret a positive sign for the velocity as motion east and a negative sign as motion west.

Our final result is that the 2 kg ball is moving west with a speed of 5.4 m/sec. after the collision and the 3 kg ball is moving east with a speed of 1.6 m/sec. after the collision.

Chapter XIX Problems

1. A gun of mass 5.6 kg fires a bullet of mass 24 grams. The velocity of the bullet after firing, is 755 m/sec. What is the recoil velocity of the gun?

2. An astronaut on a space walk has a mass of 5 slugs and is at rest relative to the space station. She is working with a tool having a mass of 0.5 slug. She accidentally throws this tool away from herself with a speed of 6 ft./sec. With what speed does the astronaut recoil?

3. An automobile having mass 1,500 kg is traveling east on an expressway at 30 m/sec. It overtakes a truck of mass 2,000 kg also traveling east and moving with a speed of 25 m/sec. The automobile read-ends the truck. The vehicles become locked together in this collision and continue east. What is the velocity of this combined mass?

4. Two balls of putty become one mass of putty in a collision. The first, of mass 6 kg, was originally moving east at 10 m/sec., and the second, of mass 4 kg, was originally moving west at 9 m/sec. What is the velocity of the total mass after the collision has occurred?

5. A wooden block of mass 30 kg is resting on an ice rink. A bullet of mass 20 grams and speed 150 m/sec. is fired into this wooden block. It becomes imbedded in the block. With what speed do the block and bullet combination begin to move on the icy surface?

6. Two large trucks undergo a direct head-on collision. One truck of mass 556 slugs was originally travelling north at 88 ft./sec. The other truck of mass 785 slugs was originally traveling south at 55 ft./sec. What is the final velocity of the wreckage after the collision has occurred if the two trucks stick together in the collision?

7. Due to a controller's error two aircraft are directed to land in opposite directions on the same runway in a fog. A Cessna 150 of mass 50 slugs and a Beechcraft Bonanza of mass 80 slugs undergo a direct head-on collision. The Beechcraft Bonanza was originally traveling north at a speed of 30 MPH and the Cessna was traveling south. The wreckage travels a distance of 20 ft. south during a time of 3.6 sec. What was the original speed of the Cessna?

8. A 3-kg ball is moving right with a speed of 3 m/sec. before a collision with a 2-kg ball originally moving left at 2 m/sec. What are the directions and speeds of the two balls after the collision?

9. A 2-kg ball is moving east with a speed of 4 m/sec. It collides with a 1-kg ball moving west with a speed of 2 m/sec. What are the directions and speeds of these balls after the collision has occurred?

10. A 2-kg ball moving right at 5 m/sec. overtakes and impacts a 1-kg ball also moving right at 2 m/sec. What are the speeds and directions of the two balls after the impact?

Chapter XX

Statics

Statics is a subject that all mechanical and aeronautical design engineers must take. The word "static" means that each part of the body is not moving relative to other parts of the body.

We recall from Newton's second law that, if a particle (some small part of a structure) is at rest, the vector sum of the forces acting on this particle must be zero. This means that there is no net or unbalanced force acting on the particle.

If the vector sum of all the forces acting on a particle is zero, the vector sum of all the forces or components of forces in the x-direction is zero and similarly, the vector sum of all the forces or components of forces in the y-direction is also zero.

We use the Greek letter Sigma (Σ) to mean "the sum of". With this notation, we can write:

$$\Sigma F_x = 0 \quad \text{and} \quad \Sigma F_y = 0$$

Also, for the x-direction, we note that forces to the right would have a positive sign, forces to the left would have a negative sign. For the y-direction, forces up would have a positive sign and forces down would have a negative sign.

Since, in both cases, the negative terms can be transposed to the opposite member of the equation, the two equations above can be written as follows:

sum of force components up
=
sum of force components down

sum of force components left
=
sum of force components right

These two equations could be written:

(1) $\quad \Sigma F_{up} = \Sigma F_{down}$
and
(2) $\quad \Sigma F_{left} = \Sigma F_{right}$

Tension in Cables and Compression in Beams

If an agent pulls on a cord or cable attached to a body, this cord or cable can exert a pull on this body.

An agent can exert either a push or a pull on a body by using a solid rod or beam.

We can summarize this by saying:

A beam can push or pull.
A cord can only pull.

Equations (1) and (2) can be used to determine the tensions in supporting cables or the compressions in beams in certain physical situations. Several examples will follow. These examples are typical of many problems in statics, a topic commonly studied in engineering courses. The design engineer must know how strong a cable or beam must be for a certain physical structure. Statics solves the problem mathematically before the structure is actually built.

Before we consider our first example, we review a theorem from plane geometry (figure 20-1). This theorem states that if two parallel lines are cut by a transversal, the alternate interior angles are equal. A diagram shows such angles. We will refer to this theorem as the "Z" rule.

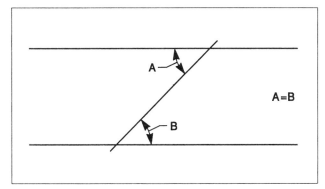

Figure 20-1.

EXAMPLE 20-A.

Determine the tensions in the cables.

The first step in the solution is to note that the knot is at rest. A new diagram, called a "free body diagram", is drawn to the right. This diagram shows a point of the structure that is at rest. In this case, we choose the knot since we know that it is at rest and all of the forces, the weight of the body and the tensions in the two cords act at this point. In the free body diagram, two little lines have been drawn through T to indicate that T has been replaced by its two components.

Note that the horizontal component of T is T cos 55°, since this component is next to the 55° angle. The vertical component of T is T sin 55°, since this component is the same length as the vector component which is opposite the 55° angle.

Now we use our two force equations:

$$F_{up} = F_{down} \qquad (1) \quad T_2 \sin 55° = 800$$

$$F_{left} = F_{right} \qquad (2) \quad T_1 = T_2 \cos 55°$$

We now have two equations in the two unknowns: T_1 and T_2. Since equation (1) involves only one unknown, we solve this equation first.

$$T_2 = \frac{800}{\sin 55°} = 977 \text{ lbs.}$$

Now we substitute this result into equation (2).

$$T_1 = (977) \cos 55°$$

$$T_1 = 560 \text{ lbs.}$$

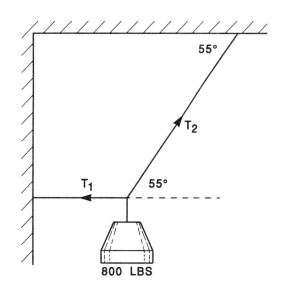

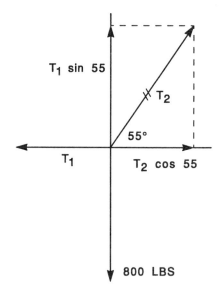

EXAMPLE 20-B.

Sometimes it is important to know the compression that will exist in a solid beam. Recall that a cable can experience only a tension. On the other hand, a beam can experience either a tension or a compression. In the following example, the beam is compressed. It pushes out at the point where the cable and the weight are attached. The free body diagram is shown to the right.

$$F_{up} = F_{down} \quad (1) \quad T \sin 47° = 700$$

$$F_{left} = F_{right} \quad (2) \quad T \cos 47° = C$$

First solve equation (1) for T.

$$T = \frac{700}{\sin 47°}$$

$$T = 957 \text{ lbs.}$$

Substitute this value into equation (2).

$$C = 957 \cos 47°$$

$$C = 653 \text{ lbs.}$$

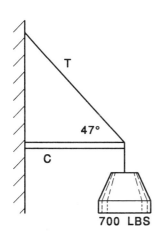

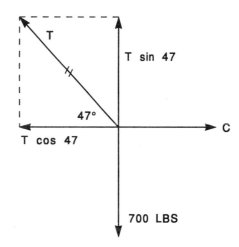

EXAMPLE 20-C.

A more complicated algebraic problem arises when the beam is not in a horizontal position. In this case, each of the equations that we write contains both unknowns. We must therefore solve either equation for either unknown and then substitute this value into the other equation. An example will clarify this method.

In the left diagram, we have put in a perpendicular and found the values of the angles it makes with the beam and the cord.

Note that there are two upward forces. We must add these two forces and set the sum equal to the downward force.

(1) $$T \sin 55° + C \sin 40° = 600$$

(2) $$T \cos 55° = C \cos 40°$$

Solve equation (2) for T:

$$T = C \frac{\cos 40°}{\cos 55°}$$

(3) $$T = 1.34 \, C$$

We next substitute this value of T into equation (1) and solve for C.

$$(1.34 \, C) \sin 55° + C \sin 40° = 600$$

$$1.098 \, C + 0.643 \, C = 600$$

$$1.741 \, C = 600$$

$$C = 345 \text{ lbs.}$$

Now we substitute this value in equation (3) to solve for T.

$$T = 1.34 \, (345)$$

$$T = 462 \text{ lbs.}$$

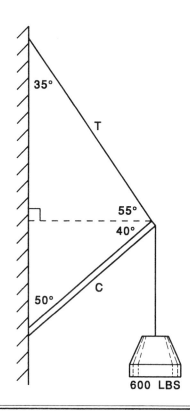

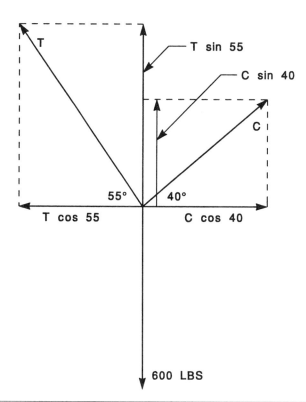

In the problems that follow, find the tensions in the cords and the compressions in the beams. Be sure to draw a free body diagram in each case. This may seem unnecessary but it is a great practical help. **A clear, carefully drawn diagram leads to correct results!**

The preceding work on statics is typical of the type of problem that needs to be solved by any design engineer including aeronautical design engineers.

Chapter XX Problems

Find the tensions in the cords and the compresions in the beams.

1.

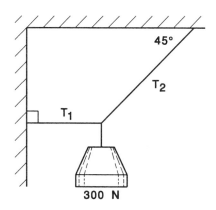

3.

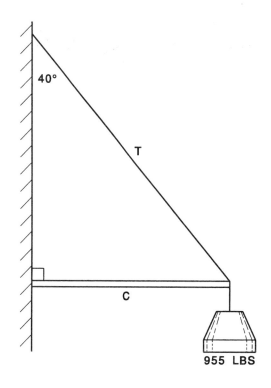

2.

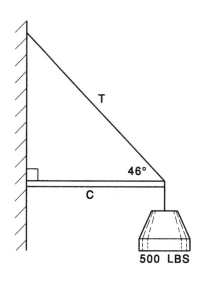

4.

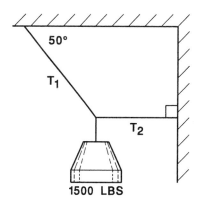

5.

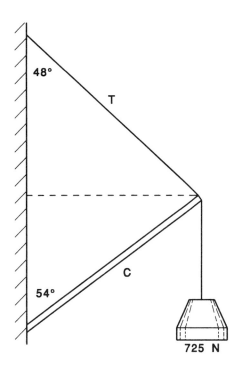

48°

T

54°

C

725 N

7.

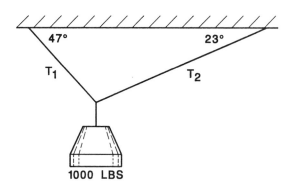

47°   23°

T₁   T₂

1000 LBS

8. The plane in the problem 7 lands at an angle of 30° and the force exerted by the earth is 80,000 lbs. Find L and R.

6.

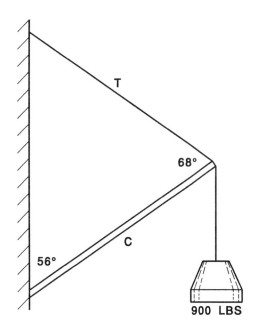

T

68°

C

56°

900 LBS

Chapter XXI

Torque, Moment of Inertia and Angular Momentum

Torque

Consider the diagrams shown below. We define torque as the force (F) applied to a body that is pivoted at a point (O) multiplied by the distance from the pivot point to the place where the force is applied, and multiplied by the sin of the angle between r and F. We will use the Greek letter Tau (τ) for torque. The distance mentioned in the preceding sentence is called the lever arm and symbolized by the letter r.

The defining equation is:

$$\tau = r\,F\,\sin\theta$$

In the diagram below, we note that $\theta = 90°$. This is by far the most common case. Since $\sin 90° = 1$, this common case reduces to the more simple equation:

$$\tau = rF$$

However, it must be remembered that in those cases where θ is not $90°$, the full equation must be used. Note also that the unit for torque is the lb.-ft.

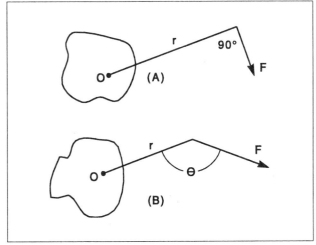

Figure 21-1.

EXAMPLE 21-A.

A worker is using a wrench to tighten a bolt. The bolt is a distance of 9″ from the place where the worker applies a force of 40 lbs. The force is applied at right angles to the wrench. What is the torque?

$$\tau = (40 \text{ lbs.})\,(0.75 \text{ ft.})\,\sin 90°$$

$$\tau = 30 \text{ lb.-ft.}$$

If, in the above example, the worker, because of an obstruction, must apply his force at an angle of 70°. What is the new torque?

$$\tau = (40 \text{ lbs.})\,(0.75 \text{ ft.})\,\sin 70° = 28.2 \text{ lb.-ft.}$$

The concept of torque is important in the study of "statics". We recall that we studied some aspects of statics in chapter 20. In chapter 20, we used two principles of equilibrium:

> The sum of the forces in the x-direction must be zero.

> The sum of the forces in the y-direction must be zero.

Now we have an additional condition for equilibrium:

> The sum of the torques must be zero.

We summarize these three equations as follows:

$$\Sigma F_{left} = \Sigma F_{right}$$

$$\Sigma F_{up} = F_{down}$$

$$\Sigma \tau_{cw} = \Sigma \tau_{ccw}$$

We note that a clockwise torque tends to cause the beam to rotate in a clockwise sense and a counterclockwise torque tends to cause a counterclockwise rotation. The use of these three equations to solve problems dealing with static equilibrium will be illustrated by the example which follows.

EXAMPLE 21-B.

A light of weight 200 lbs. hangs at the end of a horizontal beam of weight 60 lbs. and length 6 ft. The beam is uniform and has its center of gravity at its center. This means that the total weight of the beam acts as if it were concentrated at its center. A supporting cord makes an angle of 40° with the beam. Find the tension in the cord (T) and the horizontal force (H) and the vertical force (V) which the building exerts on the beam.

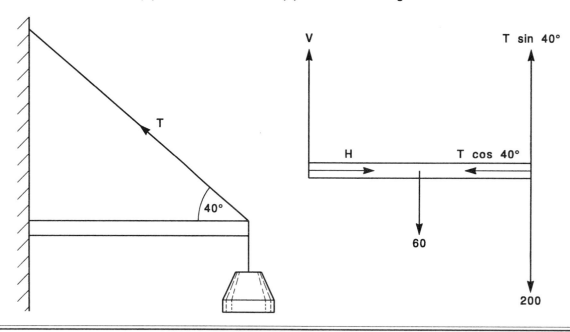

We resolve the tension in the cord into a vertical component ($T \sin 40°$) and a horizontal component ($T \cos 40°$).

We now apply the three conditions for equilibrium:

$$\Sigma F_{left} = \Sigma F_{right} \quad (1) \qquad T \cos 40° = H$$

$$\Sigma F_{up} = \Sigma F_{down} \quad (2) \quad V + T \sin 40° = 60 + 200$$

In using the torque equation we assume that the pivot point is at the left end of the beam. The lever arm for each torque can be found be finding the perpendicular distance from the pivot point to the line of action of each force. Note that forces are in pounds and distances are in feet. For simplicity we will not include units in the equation.

$$\Sigma \tau_{ccw} = \Sigma \tau_{ccw}$$

$$(3) \qquad (60)(3) + (200)(6) = (T \sin 40)(6)$$

The three forces, V, H and $T \cos 40°$, all have zero lever arms and therefore produce zero torque.

Equation (3) has only one unknown and can easily be solved.

$$\frac{180 + 1200}{(\sin 40)(6)} = T$$

$$T = 358 \text{ lbs.}$$

We next substitute this value for T into equations (1) and (2).

$$H = (358) \cos 40°$$

$$H = 274 \text{ lbs.}$$

$$V + (358)\sin 40° = 260$$

$$V = 260 - 230$$

$$V = 30 \text{ lbs.}$$

We have found the tension in the cord (358 lbs.), the vertical force the building exerts on the beam (30 lbs.) and the horizontal force the building exerts on the beam (274 lbs.). Construction engineers need to know the sizes of these forces to form safe construction designs.

146

Moment of Inertia

Moment of inertia is the angular analog of mass. Moment of inertia is to rotational motion what mass is to linear motion. We recall that mass is a measure of the resistance of a body to a change in its state of motion. The greater the mass (number of neutrons and protons in a body), the greater the force needed to change the linear velocity of that body. Compare in your mind the forces needed to impart to a bowling ball and a golf ball the same acceleration. The key equation here is Newton's second law of motion.

$$F = ma$$

We have already discussed angular acceleration, the angular analog of linear acceleration, and torque, the angular analog of force. We now need to examine the angular analog of mass.

$$T = (?) \alpha$$

In order to find this analog, let us consider the most simple body possible — a point mass (m). Let us attach to it a "weightless" rod of length (r) pivoted at the point (O) as shown in the diagram. Assume that a force (F) is applied to this mass (m). The mass will initially accelerate with a tangential linear acceleration (a_t). The equation $F = ma$, will hold.

$$F = ma_t$$

Let us multiply each side of this equation by r:

$$rF = r\, ma_t$$

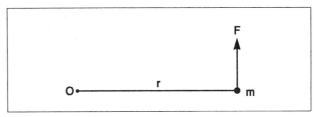

Figure 21-2.

Next, recall that rF equals the torque and that a_t equals $r\alpha$.

$$rF = r\, m(r\alpha)$$

$$\tau = (mr^2)\, \alpha$$

We will introduce the symbol I for the quantity in parentheses and call it the moment of inertia.

$$\tau = I\alpha$$

For this one point mass body, we have the relation $I = mr^2$. We note that the r in this equation is the distance of m from the pivot point, the center of the rotation.

For a body containing many point masses, the moment of inertia is the sum of each tiny mass of the body multiplied by the square of its distance to the axis of rotation. Symbolically, we write:

$$I = \Sigma\, mr^2$$

For each different geometrically shaped body there is a formula for the moment of inertia. These formulas are found by using integral calculus. We note that we do not have to derive these formulas. We accept them from the mathematicians!

Important Moments of Inertia

1. A thin circular hoop of mass (M) and radius (R) about an axis through the center and perpendicular to the plane of the hoop:

$$I = MR^2$$

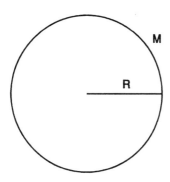

3. A sphere of mass (M) and radius (R) about an axis through the center of the sphere:

$$I = \frac{2}{5} MR^2$$

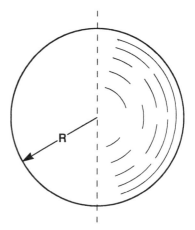

2. A circular cylinder or disk of mass (M) and radius (R) about an axis through the center and perpendicular to the plane of the disk:

$$I = \frac{1}{2} MR^2$$

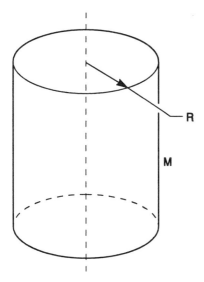

4. A rod of mass (M) and length (L) about an axis perpendicular to the rod and through its center:

$$I = \frac{1}{12} ML^2$$

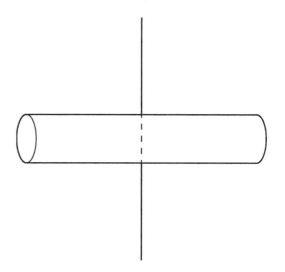

5. A rod of mass (M) and length (L) about an axis perpendicular to the rod and through its end:

$$I = \frac{1}{3}ML_2$$

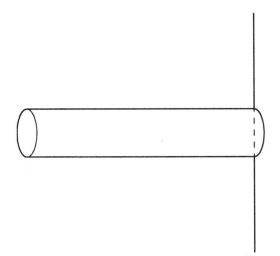

The angular analog of $F = ma$ is:

$$\tau = I\alpha$$

In this important equation we note that α must be in rad./sec.^{2} The equation requires radian measure!

Consider a disk of total mass (M) and radius (R) and compare it to a hoop (all the mass at the edge) of the **same mass and radius**. We apply to each body the equation:

$$\tau = I\alpha$$

We note that the disk has one-half the moment of inertia of the hoop. Therefore, it would require a torque twice as great to give the hoop the same angular acceleration as the disk. We can say that it is harder to accelerate the hoop than it is to accelerate the disk. This is understandable since more of the mass of the hoop is further from the axis of rotation than in the case of the disk.

Angular Momentum

We recall the definition of linear momentum. You may wish to review the material discussed in chapter 19.

$$\text{momentum} = \text{mass} \times \text{velocity}$$

In symbols, we write:

$$p = mv$$

The angular analog of linear momentum is angular momentum (L). The defining equation for angular momentum is:

$$L = I\omega$$

This equation was easy to write because we know that the angular analog for mass is moment of inertia (I) and the angular analog for linear velocity is angular velocity (ω).

In chapter 19 we discussed a basic law of physics, the conservation of linear momentum. This law tells us that, in the absence of external forces, the momentum of a system is conserved.

There is a similar law dealing with rotational motion. In the absence of external torques the angular momentum of a system is conserved. In symbols we can write:

$$I_1\omega_1 = I_2\omega_2$$

You will be surprised to discover that you have seen this law in operation many times!

A figure skater is rotating is such a way that his arms are extended away from his body. As he pulls in his arms so that his moment of inertia is decreased, his angular velocity must increase so that his angular momentum will remain constant!

An Olympic diver is rotating rapidly during one of his high dives. Before he enters the water, he extends his arms away from the axis of rotation. In this way, he increases his moment of inertia and thus he decreases his angular velocity before entering the water.

The conservation of angular momentum in action can be seen in many sporting events. Look for examples of this important law of physics as you watch your television set!

Chapter XXI Problems

1. A uniform horizontal beam of length 4 ft. and weight 500 lbs. supports a weight of 200 lbs. at its end. There is a supporting cord that makes an angle of 30 ° with the horizontal beam. Find the tension in the cord and the vertical and horizontal forces that the building exerts on the beam.

2. A uniform horizontal beam of length 8 ft. and weight 800 lbs. supports a weight of 500 lbs. at its end. There is a supporting cord that makes an angle of 40 ° with the building. Find the tension in the cord and the vertical and horizontal forces that the building exerts on the beam.

3. What is the moment of inertia of a hoop of mass 4 kg and radius 3 m?

4. What is the moment of inertia of a disk of mass 6 kg and radius 2 m?

5. A torque of 75 lb.-ft. is applied to a disk of moment of inertia of 100 slug-ft.^{2} What is the angular acceleration?

6. An Olympic skater is rotating with arms extended so that his moment of inertia is 4 slug-ft^2. and his angular velocity is 2 rad./sec. He pulls in his arms so that his moment is decreased to 3 slug-ft.^{2} What is his new angular velocity?

7. A diver has angular velocity 4 rad./sec. while his moment of inertia is 3 slug-ft.^{2} He spreads out his arms so that his new moment of inertia is 3.5 slug-ft.^{2} What is his new angular velocity?

8. The rotor of a 400 Hz alternator can be considered to be a cylinder for purposes of calculating its moment of inertia. If the mass of the rotor is 1.5 slugs and its radius is 6 ", what is its moment of inertia?

Chapter XXII

Some Properties of Solids and Liquids

Stress and Strain

Consider a metal rod suspended from an overhead support as shown in figure 22-1. The cross-sectional area of the rod is A. A force (F) is applied to this rod in a downward direction. This can easily be done by hanging a weight at the lower end. Such a force is called a longitudinal force since it is directed along the length of the rod.

We define the stress applied to the rod by the following equation:

$$\text{Stress} = \frac{F}{A}$$

A longitudinal force could also be applied in such a way that the rod would be compressed instead. The equation is the same.

If the stress tends to stretch the rod it is called a tensile stress. If the stress tends to compress the rod it is called a compressional stress.

The strain is defined as the change in length divided by the original length:

$$\text{Strain} = \frac{\Delta L}{L_o}$$

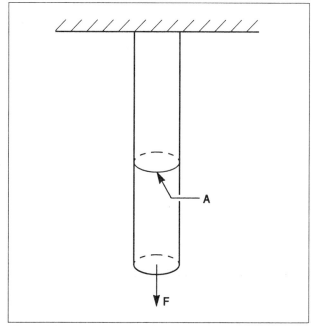

Figure 22-1.

Various materials deform more or less as longitudinal forces are applied to them. Handbooks of physics list a table of Young's Modulus (Y). See figure 22-2. Young's Modulus is defined as follows:

$$Y = \frac{\text{Stress}}{\text{Strain}} = \frac{F/A}{\Delta L/L_o}$$

A rearrangement of the complex fraction gives:

$$Y = \frac{F L_o}{A \Delta L}$$

This equation is more useful in the form:

$$\Delta L = \frac{F L_o}{A Y}$$

This equation is important because it gives us a means of predicting how much a body will stretch (or compress) when a longitudinal force is applied to the body.

EXAMPLE 22-A.

A copper rod having a cross-sectional area of 0.0033 in.^{2} and a length of 24 in. is subjected to a longitudinal force of 500 lbs. How much will the rod stretch?

$$\Delta L = \frac{(500 \text{ lbs.}) (24 \text{ in.})}{(0.0033 \text{ in.}^2) (16 \times 10^6 \text{ lbs.}/\text{in.}^2)}$$

$$\Delta L = 0.227 \text{ in.}$$

The above material deals with rods or one-dimensional solid bodies. Such rods can be subjected to a tensile stress where the length is increased or a compressional stress where the length is decreased. Solid bodies can also be subjected to compressional pressures on all sides, as in the case of a body under water. In the case of liquids, only compressional stresses are possible. We can't stretch a liquid! Therefore for liquids and solid bodies, we discuss change of volume relative to the initial volume.

The equation is similar:

$$\Delta V = \frac{F V_o}{A B}$$

In this equation, B is the "bulk modulus". Tables of B are also listed in handbooks of physics. The equation is more practical if we note that pressure is F/A. Usually we know the pressure rather than the force and the area.

The useful form of the equation is:

$$\Delta V = \frac{p V_o}{B}$$

It should be noted that ΔV is always a decrease in volume.

EXAMPLE 22-B.

A brass body of volume 460 in.^{3} is subjected to a pressure of 50 lb./in.^{2} What is the decrease in volume of this body?

$$\Delta V = \frac{(50 \text{ lb.}/\text{in.}^2) \ (460 \text{ in.}^3)}{8.5 \times 10^6 \text{ lb.}/\text{in.}^2}$$

$$\Delta V = 0.0027 \text{ in.}^3$$

YOUNG MODULUS, Y		BULK MODULUS, B
MATERIAL	(LB./IN.^{2})	(LB./IN.^{2})
Aluminum	10×10^6	10×10^6
Brass	13×10^6	8.5×10^6
Copper	16×10^6	17×10^6
Glass	7.8×10^6	5.2×10^6
Iron	13×10^6	1.45×10^6
Steel	29×10^6	23×10^6
Ethyl Alcohol		0.16×10^6
Oil		0.25×10^6
Water		0.31×10^6
Mercury		4.0×10^6

Figure 22-2.

Elastic Limit and Ultimate Strength

The elastic limit, is defined as the maximum stress that can be applied to a material before it will be permanently deformed. Within the elastic limit a body will return to its original size and shape after the stress has been removed.

The ultimate strength is defined as the maximum stress that can be applied to a material before it will rupture.

EXAMPLE 22-C.

The elastic limit for copper is 2.3×10^4 lb./in.^{2} and the ultimate strength is 4.9×10^4 lb./in.^{2} Suppose that a copper rod has a cross-sectional area of 0.5 in.^{2} A force of 11,500 lbs. applied longitudinally to this rod would just be within the elastic limit. A force of 12,000 lbs. would deform the rod in such a way that it would not return to it original size after the force is removed. A force of 24,500 lbs. would cause the rod to rupture.

Torsion Forces

Torsion forces cause rods to twist.

Ductility

Substances that can be drawn out into thin wires are said to be ductile.

Malleability

Substances that can be hammered into thin sheets are said to be malleable.

ELASTIC LIMIT		ULTIMATE STRENGTH
MATERIAL	(LB./IN.^{2})	(LB./IN.^{2})
Aluminum	1.9×10^4	2.1×10^4
Brass	5.5×10^4	6.6×10^4
Copper	2.3×10^4	4.9×10^4
Iron	2.4×10^4	4.7×10^4
Annealed Steel	3.6×10^4	7.1×10^4
Spring Steel	6.0×10^4	10×10^4

Figure 22-3.

152

Chapter XXII Problems

1. A steel bolt with a cross-sectional area of 0.067 in.^{2} and a length of 6.0″ is subjected to a force of 450 lbs. What is the increase in length of the bolt?

2. An iron body of volume 67 in.^{3} is subjected to a pressure of 670 lb./in.^{2} What is the decrease in volume of this body?

3. A copper rod has a cross-sectional area of 0.046 in.^{2} and a length of 24″. What longitudinal force must be applied to cause this rod to stretch by 0.0056 in.?

4. A brass rod has a cross-sectional area of 0.25 in.^{2} What longitudinal force must be applied to cause this rod to rupture?

5. An aluminum brace inside a wing of a plane has a cross-sectional area of 0.25 in.^{2} What is the greatest longitudinal force that can be applied to the brace without causing the brace to be permanently deformed?

6. A steel hydraulic piston has a cross-sectional area of 0.4 in.^{2} and a length of 20 inches. A compressive longitudinal force of 5,000 lbs. is applied to the piston. What is the decrease in length of the piston?

7. (a) If a compressive force of 35,000 lbs. causes an aluminum brace inside the wing of a plane to rupture, what is the cross-sectional area of the brace?

   (b) What cross-sectional area is necessary so that the brace will neither rupture nor be permanently deformed when such a force is applied?

8. A steel hydraulic piston has a cross-sectional area of 0.355 in.^{2} and a length of 21.3″. A compressive force of 4,800 lbs. is applied to the piston. What is the decrease in length of the piston?

9. A steel body is lowered into ocean water. Its volume at sea level is 250 ft.^{3} What is the decrease in volume when the body is at a depth of 12,000 ft.?

10. An aluminum body is lowered to a depth of 2,000 ft. in ocean water. If its volume at the surface of the ocean is 35 ft.^{3}, what is its volume at this new depth?

11. A brace made of spring steel ruptures when a compressive force of 45,000 lbs is applied to it. What is the cross-sectional area of this brace? What cross-sectional area is necessary so that the brace will neither rupture nor be permanently deformed when a force of this magnitude is applied?

Chapter XXIII

Wave Motion

There are many types of waves: light waves, sound waves, radio waves, cosmic rays, x-rays, communication waves, waves on cords, etc. In our first discussion of waves, we will deal with that type which is called just "wave", that is, a water wave.

Let us assume that a stone is thrown into the middle of a large, calm pond on a day when there is no wind. If there is a perpendicular plane surface cutting the water surface through a point where

the stone hits the water, an observer would see the water surface disturbed in such a way that a curve would be visible. This curve would have a shape as shown in figure 23-1.

In figure 23-1 it is important to note that the pattern of crests and troughs is moving. If the stone hits the water surface at the point (P), the pattern is moving to the right in the diagram above. Of course, the entire pattern is moving out from point (P) in all directions, but we are looking in only one direction. We should also note that the pattern is moving with a definite speed, called the wave speed (v).

The amplitude (A) of the wave is the greatest displacement from the rest position. The amplitude is shown in figure 23-1.

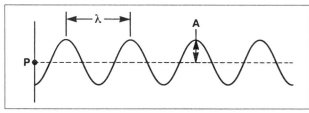

Figure 23-1.

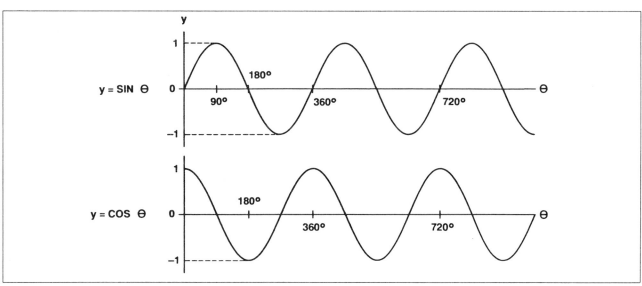

Figure 23-2.

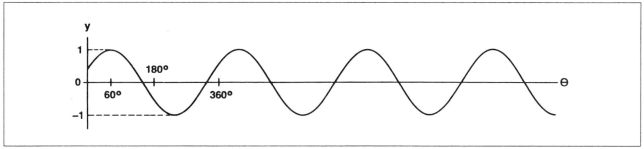

Figure 23-3.

Another distance that we will need in our discussion of waves is the wavelength, λ (Greek letter lambda). The wavelength is defined as the distance from one point on the wave pattern to the next point in a similar position. The distance from the top of a crest to the top of the next crest is a wavelength. Also the distance from the bottom of one trough to the bottom of the next trough is also the same distance, one wavelength. The distance (λ) is also shown in the diagram.

In our study of wave motion we need to describe this wavy pattern with an exact mathematical expression. There are two curves that are well known from our study of trigonometry. In figure 23-2 are the graphs of the two important equations $y = \sin \theta$ and $y = \cos \theta$. In these two equations, θ can be in degrees or in radians. We will use degrees since most of us think more readily in these units!

Your calculators know all about these two curves. Try out some of the calculations which produce points for the graphing of these two curves.

Note that, for the sine curve, the vertical axis occurs at a point where $y = 0$. For the cosine curve the vertical axis occurs at a point where $y = 1$. There is a more general curve, called "sinusoidal", where the shape of the curve is the same as in the case of the sine or cosine curve but the vertical axis has a general orientation. We would like to have a mathematical representation for this general case. Figure 23-3 is a graph of the more general case.

The equation is:

$$y = \sin (\theta + 30°)$$

Try out some values on your calculator!

EXAMPLE 23-A.

The graph of the equation $y = 2 \sin (\theta + 60°)$ is shown below:

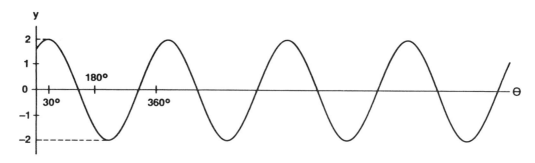

The graph of the equation $y = 3 \sin (\theta + 45°)$ is shown below:

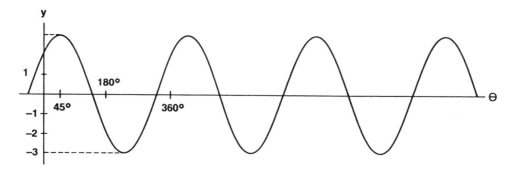

Sometimes we want to express y as a function of the distance from the origin (x) instead of a function of the angle (θ). The equation for this case is as follows:

$$y = A \sin \left(\frac{360\,x}{\lambda} + \Phi\right)$$

In figure 23-3, 30° is known as the "phase angle". Of course, the phase angle can be any other angle as well. Usually, we use the symbol Φ (Greek letter Phi) for the phase angle. To be more general, we should write the equation in the following manner:

$$y = \sin(\theta + \Phi)$$

There is one other modification that we should make in the equation. The greatest y value may not be one. We can modify our equation by inserting the factor A, representing the amplitude, into the right member. Our equation now has the most general form:

$$y = A \sin(\theta + \Phi)$$

EXAMPLE 23-B.

A stone is thrown into a pool of water. This causes a water wave to move out in all directions. In one direction, the water wave has amplitude 0.6 ft. and wavelength 0.8 ft. Write the equation of this wave.

$$y = 0.6 \sin\left(\frac{360\,x}{0.8} + \Phi\right)$$

At an instant after the stone has been thrown into the water, the phase angle has the value 30°, what is the equation of the wave at this instant?

$$y = 0.6 \sin\left(\frac{360\,x}{0.8} + 30°\right)$$

At this same instant, a floating leaf is 20 ft. from the source of the disturbance. What is the displacement (up or down from its rest position) of this leaf?

$$y = 0.6 \sin\left[\frac{360(20)}{0.8} + 30°\right]$$

$$y = 0.3 \text{ ft.}$$

From our observations of real water waves, we know that the wave gradually dies out due to fluid friction of the water. In our problems, we have neglected this attenuation of the amplitude.

We now have the mathematical tools to represent the one dimensional instantaneous equation of a wave that is moving in the positive x-direction. This equation is:

$$y = A \sin\left(\frac{360\,x}{\lambda} + \Phi\right)$$

The above equation applies to all types of waves.

Let us next consider sinusoidal wave motion impressed on a very long flexible cord by an oscillating body. Assume that the oscillating body is a sphere attached to a vertical spring. After the spring has been oscillating for some time, the physical situation is as shown in figure 23-4.

The frequency (f) of the oscillating body is defined as the number of complete oscillations in one second. Frequency is expressed in cycles/sec. or Hertz. The period (T) is defined as the time for one complete oscillation. It is expressed in seconds.

Let us suppose that the oscillating body completes 6 oscillations in one second. It follows that the time for one oscillation is one-sixth of a second.

In this case:

$$f = 6\,\text{Hz} \qquad \text{and} \qquad T = \frac{1}{6}\,\text{sec.}$$

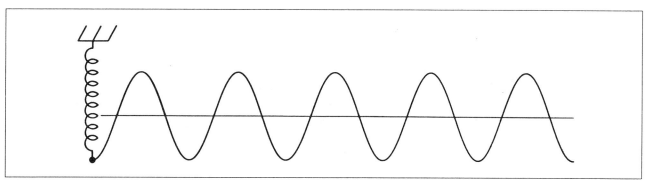

Figure 23-4.

From this example we see that f and T are reciprocals of each other.

$$T = \frac{1}{f} \qquad \text{and} \qquad f = \frac{1}{T}$$

We next seek a relationship between wave speed (v), frequency (f), and wavelength (λ).

We note that the wave moves forward a distance of one wavelength in a time of one period. Of course, the wave moves with speed (v).

Since the distance equals the speed times the time, we can write the equation:

$$\lambda = v\,T$$

From this equation, we have:

$$\frac{\lambda}{T} = v$$

And finally:

$$f\lambda = v$$

$$v = f\lambda$$

EXAMPLE 23-C.

(a) A body oscillates with a frequency of 8 Hz, and sends out a wave having a wavelength of 0.2 ft. What is the speed of the wave?

$$v = (8\ \frac{\text{cycles}}{\text{sec.}})\,(0.2\ \text{ft.}) = 1.6\ \text{ft./sec.}$$

(b) What is the wavelength of a wave moving with a speed of 5 ft./sec. if the frequency of the oscillating body which is the source of the wave is 12 Hz?

$$\lambda = \frac{v}{f} = \frac{5\ \text{ft./sec.}}{12\ \text{cycles/sec.}} = 0.417\ \text{ft.}$$

(c) An observer times the speed of a water wave to be 2 ft./sec. and notes that the wavelength is 0.5 ft. What is the frequency of the disturbance that gives rise to this wave?

$$f = \frac{v}{\lambda} = \frac{2\ \text{ft./sec.}}{0.5\ \text{ft.}} = 4\ \frac{\text{cycles}}{\text{sec.}} = 4\ \text{Hz}$$

Resonance

In the case of water waves and in the case of waves on a very long cord, we were able to neglect waves that were reflected back along the medium. We now must consider reflected waves.

The most common example is the case of waves originating in a disturbance impressed on a cord or string of a definite length. Many musical instruments depend on such vibrations.

If a sinusoidal disturbance is impressed on a very long cord a sinusoidal wave travels continuously along the cord. However, if the sinusoidal wave meets a fixed end, a reflected wave moves back along the cord.

The wave patterns which are observed are called the normal modes of vibration of the cord. In figure 23-5, the length of the cord is L. The wavelength in the various modes of vibration are λ. The n is the index of the mode. In the equations which follow, n has an integral value, that is n = 1, 2, 3, 4. . .

We can write a general relation as follows:

$$\lambda_n = \frac{2}{n} L$$

The vibration where n = 1 is called the fundamental mode of vibration of the body. The other vibrations are called overtone vibrations. Every body which can vibrate has a certain fundamental mode of vibration of a definite frequency. If this frequency is impressed on the body, it will vibrate with a relatively large amplitude. We say that the body is vibrating in resonance with the impressed frequency.

Designers of aircraft must be seriously concerned about the phenomenon of resonant frequency because if a certain component of an airplane or helicopter is caused to vibrate at its resonant frequency the amplitude of the vibration can become very large and the component will destroy itself by vibration.

Let us examine the case of a helicopter which has a tail boom with a natural or resonant frequency of 1 Hz. That is, if you were to strike the boom with your fist it would oscillate once each second. The normal rotational speed of the main rotor is 400 RPM and the helicopter has 3 blades on its main rotor. Each time a rotor blade moves over the tail boom the blade is going to cause a downward pulse of air to strike the tail boom. The designer must determine the speed at which the pulses will be equal to the resonant frequency of the boom. One cycle per second is equivalent to 60 cycles/minute. Since each of the three blades causes a pulse each revolution, there will be 3 × 60 or 180 pulses/minute. Therefore a rotor speed of 180 RPM would be critical and the pilot would be warned against operating at that speed. Since the boom also has a secondary, or overtone, resonant frequency of twice the fundamental resonant frequency, 360 RPM would also have to be avoided but would not be as critical as 180 RPM. The third frequency of concern would be 3 × 180 or 540, but that is above the rotor operating speed, so is not a problem.

The natural frequency of vibration is also an extremely important consideration in designing the wings, horizontal and vertical stabilizers of an airplane. The designer must be certain that the resonant frequency when the surface is bent is different from that resonant frequency when it is twisted. If that is not the case, an aerodynamic interaction with the elasticity of the surface can result in "flutter" which can cause the surface to fracture in a fraction of a second after it begins.

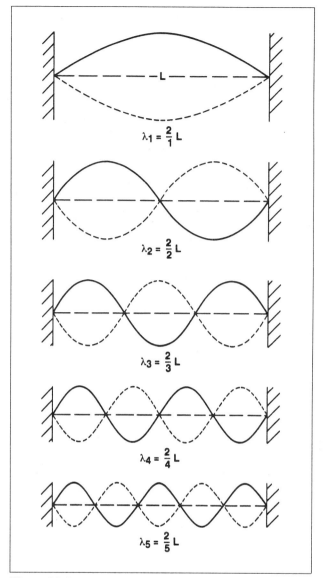

Figure 23-5.

Chapter XXIII Problems

1. A water wave has amplitude 1.5 ft. and wave length 1.1 ft. What is the equation of this wave at an instant when the phase angle is 25°?

2. At this same instant, what is the displacement of a floating body that is 40 ft. from the source of the disturbance?

3. A water wave has a wavelength of 0.9 ft. and the wavespeed is 4 ft./sec. What is the frequency of the disturbance setting up this wave?

4. A wave on a cord is set up by a body oscillating at 12 Hz. The wavelength is 0.25 ft. What is the wavespeed?

5. A water wave is set up by a source oscillating at 13 Hz. The speed of the wave is 15 ft./sec. What is the wavelength?

6. An observer notes that a water wave has an amplitude of 0.2 ft. and a wavelength of 0.8 ft. What is the equation of the wave if we assume that, at the time in question, the phase angle is 0 °?

7. In the above problem, what is the displacement of a floating leaf at a distance of 11.9 ft. from the source of the wave?

Chapter XXIV

Light

Light is a form of electromagnetic radiation. There is a certain band of frequency of electromagnetic radiation that affects the retina of the human eye. We call this band of radiation "visible light". Sometimes the word "light" means only visible light and sometimes the word "light" is used as a generic word to mean any kind of electromagnetic radiation. Electromagnetic radiation is a type of wave. As in the case of all wave motion, the wave moves with a definite speed (c) called the speed of light. The speed of light has been measured many times and has the value, to three significant digits, 3.00×10^8 m/sec.

The wavelength of visible light is usually measured in a unit called the Angstrom (A).

$$1 \text{ A} = 10^{-10} \text{m}$$

Various colors of visible light have characteristic wavelengths.

Figure 24-1 is a list of some colors and their approximate wavelengths.

Wavelengths of electromagnetic radiation shorter than 4,000 A are not visible and are called "ultraviolet" and wavelengths longer than 7,000 A are also not visible and are called "infrared".

We also note that "colors" such as "blue-green" also exist. The wavelength would be about 5,000 A. Colors gradually change as the wavelength changes.

As in the case of all wave motion, the speed of electromagnetic radiation equals the frequency times the wavelength. Therefore, for light, we have the relation:

$$c = f \lambda$$

VIOLET	4500 A
BLUE	4800 A
GREEN	5200 A
YELLOW	5800 A
ORANGE	6000 A
RED	6400 A

Figure 24-1.

FREQUENCY IN HERTZ		WAVELENGTH IN METERS
10^{23}	COSMIC RAYS	10^{-14}
10^{22}		10^{-13}
10^{21}	GAMMA RAYS	10^{-12}
10^{20}		10^{-11}
10^{19}	X-RAYS	10^{-10}
10^{18}		10^{-9}
10^{17}	ULTRAVIOLET	10^{-8}
10^{16}		10^{-7}
10^{15}	VISIBLE	10^{-6}
10^{14}		10^{-5}
10^{13}	INFRARED	10^{-4}
10^{12}		10^{-3}
10^{11}		10^{-2}
10^{10}	MICROWAVES/ RADAR	10^{-1}
10^{9}		1
10^{8}	TELEVISION/ FM RADIO	10^{1}
10^{7}	SHORTWAVE RADIO	10^{2}
10^{6}	AM RADIO	10^{3}
10^{5}	MARITIME COMMUINICATIONS	10^{4}
10^{4}		

Figure 24-2.

In figure 24-2, we list some common types of electromagnetic radiation with ranges of frequency and wavelength. Note that the above equation is always satisfied. As the frequency increases, the wavelength decreases in such a way that the product equals the speed of light (3×10^8 m/sec.).

In order to obtain a visual picture of electromagnetic radiation, we need to review what we already know about electric and magnetic fields.

An electric field can be pictured by considering first a single positive charge in space. Such a charge at rest sets up what is called an electric field. The electric lines of force give the direction of the force on a very small positive test charge placed in the vicinity of the charge (Q). See figure 24-3.

If we have an electric dipole, equal positive and negative charges, the electric field is somewhat more complicated and is pictured in figure 24-4.

More complex combinations of charges at rest also have in their vicinity electric fields which can be pictured by drawing electric lines of force (see figure 24-5).

We have just noted that charges at rest set up electric fields which are pictured by means of electric field lines called **E** lines. We next consider charges in motion. Charges in motion set up magnitic field lines called **B** lines.

In figure 24-6, we see the cross section of a wire carrying a current of electrons into the paper. The circular magnetic field lines (**B** lines) are shown.

We review that charges at rest set up electric field lines (**E** lines) and that charges in motion set up magnetic field lines (**B** lines).

Electromagnetic waves originate always in charges moving back and forth in some type of a transmitter. We can think of a transmitter as a straight line conductor along which electric charges move up and down or back and forth. As the charges change direction at the ends of the transmitter, they are momentarily at rest. And of course, at other times, they are moving and always accelerating. In a transmitter, therefore, charges are both sometimes in motion and sometimes at rest. A transmitter is therefore a source of both **E** lines and **B** lines. The electric and magnetic field lines escape from the transmitter and move into free space with speed (c).

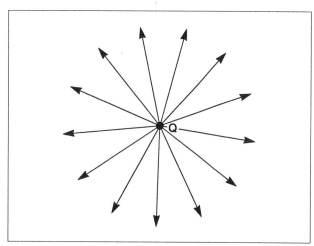

Figure 24-3.

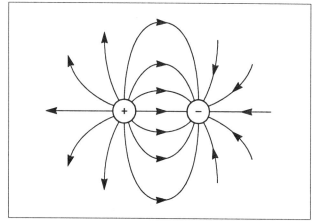

Figure 24-4.

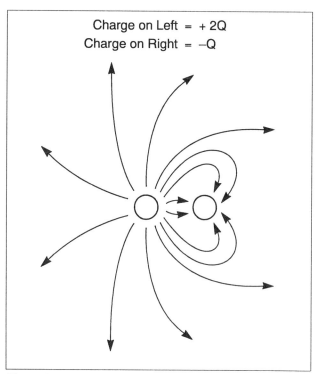

Charge on Left = + 2Q
Charge on Right = −Q

Figure 24-5.

162

Figure 24-7 is an instantaneous picture of electromagnetic radiation.

The direction of propagation is to the right. We see that both the electric field lines and magnetic field lines vary sinusoidally. The electric field lines lie in a plane that is perpendicular to the plane of the magnetic field lines. All light radiation, or electromagnetic (EM) radiation, consists of these patterns of electric and magnetic field lines moving in free space (vacuum) with speed (c) or in some other transparent medium. We note that the frequencies and wavelengths of the various types of EM radiation vary greatly.

EXAMPLE 24-A.

(a) The frequency of an x-ray is 5 × 10 Hz. What is the wavelength of this radiation?

$$c = f \lambda$$

$$\lambda = \frac{c}{f} = \frac{3 \times 10^8 \text{m/sec.}}{5 \times 10^{18} \text{c/sec.}}$$

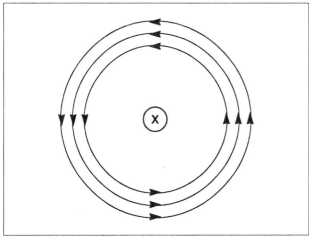

Figure 24-6.

$$\lambda = 0.6 \times 10^{-10} \text{m}$$

$$\lambda = 6 \times 10^{-11} \text{m}$$

(b) An FM radio wave has a wavelength of 6 m. What is the frequency in megahertz?

$$f = \frac{c}{\lambda}$$

$$f = \frac{3 \times 10^8 \text{m/sec.}}{6 \text{m}}$$

$$f = 50 \times 10^6 \text{ Hz} \times \frac{1 \text{ megahertz}}{10^6 \text{ Hz}}$$

$$f = 50 \text{ megahertz}$$

The Speed of Light in Various Substances

We have already stated that the speed of light in vacuum (free space) is, to three significant digits, 3.00×10^8 m/sec. The speed of light is less in various transparent substances. We define the "index of refraction" (n) as the ratio of the speed of light in vacuum to the speed of light in the substance (v).

$$n = \frac{c}{v}$$

From this equation, we see that we can find the speed (v) in various transparent substances by using the relation:

$$v = \frac{c}{n}$$

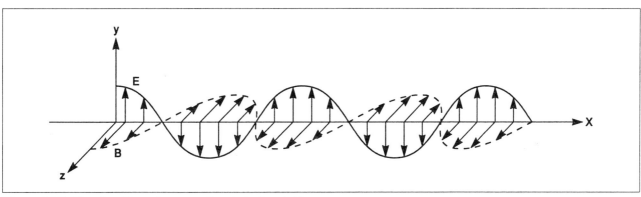

Figure 24-7. The direction of propagation is to the right.

163

EXAMPLE 24-B.

Find the speed of light in water.

$$v = \frac{3.00 \times 10^8 m/sec.}{1.33}$$

$$v = 2.25 \times 10^8 m/sec.$$

MATERIAL	n (INDEX OF REFRACTION)
INDICES OF REFRACTION FOR VARIOUS SUBSTANCES	
Air	1.00029
Benzene	1.50
Carbon Dioxide	1.00045
Diamond	2.42
Ethyl Alcohol	1.36
Glass, Crown	1.50
Glass, Flint	1.70
Ice	1.31
Water	1.33

Figure 24-8.

Chapter XXIV Problems

1. What is the wavelength in meters of an FM radio wave having a frequency of 95 mHz?

2. What is the frequency of an x-ray having a wavelength of 4×10^{-10} m?

3. What is the frequency in kilohertz of an AM radio transmission if the wavelength is 500m? (1 kHz = 1,000 Hz)

4. Find the speed of light in crown glass.

5. The speed of light in carbon tetrachloride is measured to be 2.05×10^8 m/sec. What is the index of refraction of carbon tetrachloride?

6. Find the speed of light in a diamond.

Chapter XXV

The Doppler Effect

The "Doppler effect" is named after Christian Doppler (1803-1853), the American physicist who first named the effect.

The effect is present for all wave motion. However, we will describe it for sound waves since it is most easily understood for a case where it can be observed (**heard** might be a better word).

Whenever you have stood on a railway platform and a train blows its whistle as it approaches, passes, and recedes, you have heard the Doppler effect. In this case, the sound suddenly changes from a higher pitch (frequency) as the source of sound approaches to a lower pitch as the source of sound recedes from your ear at rest on the station platform. The change in pitch occurs at the instant the train passes. Before this instant the source of sound was approaching your ear and after this instant, the source of sound is receding from your ear.

In figure 25-1, the source of sound is at the point (P) and is moving toward an ear at rest at the right of the diagram.

Let the speed of the source be called v_s and the speed of sound be v. Also let the frequency of the source be f. Since the ear receives move waves per second because of the approaching source the frequency that is heard by the ear is not the same as the frequency of the sound that is emitted by the source. The frequency that is heard will be symbolized by f'. The equation is as follows:

$$f' = \frac{v}{v - v_s} f$$

In the above equation, note that the denominator of the fraction in the right member is smaller than the numerator $(v - v_s)$ and is less than v. The magnitude of this fraction is more than one, and therefore, f' is greater than f. The observed frequency is greater than the frequency emitted by the source. Also note that the wavelength received by the ear is less than the wavelength emitted by the source.

Now assume that the ear is still at the right of the diagram. However, the source is moving to the left. The source is receding from the ear (see figure 25-2). The equation is:

$$f' = \frac{v}{v + v_s} f$$

In this case, the denominator of the fraction is greater than the numerator and value of the fraction is less than one and f' is less than f. Also, the wavelength received by the ear is greater than the wavelength emitted by the source.

There is still one other problem to be considered. Suppose that the source is at rest and the ear is moving. Consider the figure 25-3.

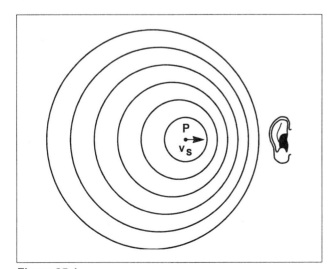

Figure 25-1.

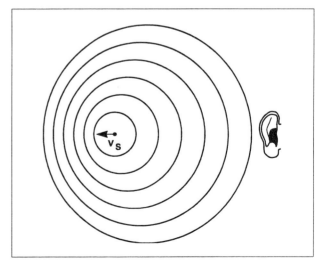

Figure 25-2.

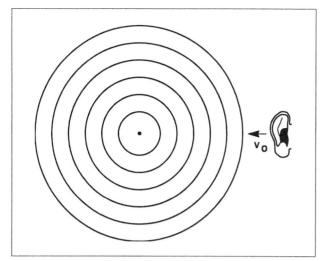

Figure 25-3.

As the ear moves to the left, it picks up more waves than it normally would if it were at rest. Let v_0 be the velocity of the observer. The equation is:

$$f' = \frac{v + v_0}{v} f$$

Note that the value of the fraction is more than one and f' is greater than f.

If the observer moves away from the source, the ear picks up less waves than it would if it were at rest.

The equation is:

$$f' = \frac{v - v_0}{v} f$$

As a conclusion, note that the ear hears a higher frequency if source and observer approach each other. Also, the ear hears a lower frequency if the source and observer recede from each other.

One equation is sufficient for all cases:

$$f' = \frac{v \pm v_0}{v \mp v_s} f$$

The upper signs in the numerator and the denominator refer to the case where the observer and source approach each other. Similarly, the lower signs refer to the case where observer and source recede from each other.

EXAMPLE 25-A.

On a day when the temperature is 85°F, a factory worker is traveling toward his place of employment at a speed of 55 MPH. The factory whistle is blowing and emitting a sound of frequency 256 Hz. What frequency is heard by the worker?

In this case, the velocity of the source (v_s) is zero (the factory whistle is not moving). The velocity of the sound (v) can be calculated. We recall the formula for the calculation of the speed of sound at various temperatures (see chapter 13).

$$v = 1087 + 1.1\,(85 - 32)$$

$$v = 1145 \text{ ft./sec.}$$

The velocity of the observer must also be expressed in ft./sec.

$$v_0 = 55 \text{ MPH} \times \frac{1.47 \text{ ft./sec.}}{1 \text{ MPH}} = 81 \text{ ft./sec.}$$

We choose the top signs in the numerator and denominator of the formula because the source and observer are approaching each other (the worker is on his way to work).

$$f' = \frac{1145 + 81}{1145 - 0}\,(256 \text{ Hz}) = 274 \text{ Hz}$$

We note that the worker hears a higher sound than that actually emitted by the factory whistle.

EXAMPLE 25-B.

A Lewis University aviation student stands at a railway crossing watching a train go by. The train, traveling at 70 MPH, is blowing its whistle at a frequency of 400 Hz. It is winter and the temperature is 10°F. What frequency does the student hear as the train approaches? What frequency does he hear as the train recedes?

The speed of the sound (v) is calculated:

$$v = 1087 + 1.1\,(10 - 32)$$

$$v = 1063 \text{ ft./sec.}$$

$$v_0 = 0 \text{ (the student is at rest)}$$

$$v_s = 70 \text{ MPH} \times \frac{1.47 \text{ ft./sec.}}{1 \text{ MPH}} = 103 \text{ ft./sec.}$$

When the train is approaching (using the top signs):

$$f' = \frac{1063 + 0}{1063 - 103}(400 \text{ Hz}) = 443 \text{ Hz}$$

When the train is receding (using the bottom signs):

$$f' = \frac{1063 - 0}{1063 + 103}(400 \text{ Hz}) = 365 \text{ Hz}$$

Doppler Radar

The Doppler effect also occurs when the waves are radio waves instead of sound waves. The equations are the same. However, in this case, the speed of the wave is the speed of an electromagnetic wave.

We express this wave speed as c and note that $c = 3 \times 10^8$ m/sec.

The Doppler formula becomes:

$$f' = \frac{c \pm v_0}{c \mp v_s} f$$

The Doppler effect with radio waves is used by state patrolmen to determine the speed of fleeing or approaching automobiles! The radio wave (of a known frequency) is sent out by the patrolman to the car under inspection. During this process, the source is at rest and the car is a moving observer (or reflector). When the wave is reflected by the car, the Doppler formula is used again. However, in this return case, the source (the moving car acting as a reflector) is in motion and the observer (the patrolman in his patrol car) is at rest.

We will define our frequencies carefully:

f = radio wave frequency sent out by the patrolman

f' = radio wave frequency arriving at and reflected by the car

f'' = radio wave frequency arriving back at the patrolman

Δf = the difference in frequency between the wave sent and the wave arriving back at the patrolman

$\Delta f = f'' - f$

We will assume that the car whose speed is to be determined is traveling **toward** the patrolman.

Since the car is the reflector, we will call its speed v_R.

$$f' = \frac{c + v_R}{c - 0} f$$

For the reflected wave:

$$f'' = \frac{c + 0}{c - v_R} f'$$

We next substitute the value of f' from the first equation into the second equation.

$$f'' = \left(\frac{c}{c - v_R}\right)\left(\frac{c + v_R}{c}\right) f$$

After cancelling c, we obtain:

$$f'' = \frac{c + v_R}{c - v_R} f$$

Now $\Delta f = f'' - f$. Therefore, to find Δf, we subtract f from each member of the above equation:

$$\Delta f = f'' - f = \frac{c + v_R}{c - v_R} f - f$$

We factor the right member of this equation and obtain:

$$\Delta f = f\left(\frac{c + v_R}{c - v_R} - 1\right)$$

Next, we find a common denominator for the terms in the parenthesis in the right member:

$$\Delta f = f\left[\frac{c + v_R - (c - v_R)}{c - v_R}\right]$$

$$\Delta f = f\left(\frac{2v_R}{c - v_R}\right)$$

In the denominator, we neglect v_R relative to c since it is so very much smaller. We finally write the relationship:

$$\Delta f = \frac{2 f v_R}{c}$$

In the above derivation, the car whose speed was to be determined was approaching the patrolman. The frequency difference was a positive number. That is, f″ was greater than f.

If the car is fleeing from the patrolman, the frequency difference ($\Delta f = f'' - f$), will be a negative number. That is, the returning frequency (f″) will be less than f (the frequency sent out by the patrolman).

Since we want to know the speed of the car, it is more helpful to write to solve the equation for v_R.

We write:

$$v_R = \frac{c \, \Delta f}{2f}$$

We review the meanings of the above symbols:

c = the speed of light = 3×10^8 m/sec.

f = the frequency of the radio waves sent out by the patrolman

$\Delta f = f'' - f =$ the difference between the frequency sent and the frequency received at the patrol car

If Δf is positive, the car is approaching.

If Δf is negative, the car is fleeing.

EXAMPLE 25-C.

A state patrolman on Interstate 80 sends out a radio wave signal of frequency 2×10^9 Hz. He points it at an approaching car. The returning signal is greater than the signal sent. The frequency difference (Δf) is 533 Hz. What is the speed of the car?

$$v_R = \frac{(3 \times 10^8 \text{ m/sec.}) \, (533 \text{ Hz})}{2(2 \times 10^9 \text{ Hz})} = 40 \text{ m/sec.}$$

$$v_R = 40 \text{ m/sec.} \times \frac{1 \text{ MPH}}{0.447 \text{ m/sec.}} = 89 \text{ MPH}$$

Ground Speed Measurement Using the Doppler Effect

The above theory assumes that the source of radiation is as rest and the reflector is moving. The derivation could be applied to a case where the source of radiation is moving and the reflector is at rest. In this case, the symbol v will replace v_R and will indicate the **relative** velocity of source and reflector.

Ground speed measurements are made by using the Doppler method. Of course, in this case, the source of the radiation (the plane) is in motion, and the v of the Doppler formula indicates the velocity of the plane relative to the ground.

The Doppler theory also assumes that the direction of the emitted electromagnetic radiation and the direction of the moving source are along the same straight line. Some modification must be made in the Doppler formula if it is to be used to determine ground speed! If the radiation is sent in the same direction as the direction of travel of the plane, no radiation would be reflected by the earth, and, therefore, no measurements could be made. The problem is solved by emitting the radiation at a depression angle (θ) and incorporating the cosine of θ into the Doppler formula. If v is the speed of the plane, v cos θ is the component of this velocity is the direction of the emitted radiation. The diagram is shown in figure 25-4.

The Doppler formula holds as before with one simple substitution. The component of the velocity of the plane in the direction of the emitted radiation becomes the new left member of the Doppler formula.

The modified Doppler formula is as follows:

$$v \cos \theta = \frac{c \, \Delta f}{2f}$$

If we solve for v (the ground speed of the plane) we obtain:

$$v = \frac{c \, \Delta f}{2f \cos \theta}$$

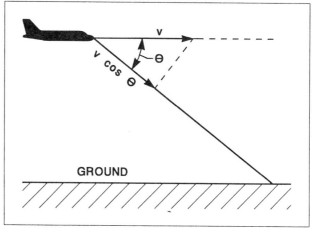

Figure 25-4.

EXAMPLE 25-D.

An aircraft uses Doppler equipment with an angle of depression of 60°. The frequency of the emitted radiation 7,500 MHz and the observed frequency shift is 6 kHz. What is the ground speed of the plane in m/sec. and in MPH?

First we must change the frequency difference from kHz to MHz. Details of this change of units will be shown:

$$\Delta f = 6 \ \cancel{kHz} \times \frac{10^3 \ \cancel{Hz}}{1 \ \cancel{kHz}} \times \frac{1 \ MHz}{10^6 \ \cancel{Hz}}$$

$$\Delta f = 0.006 \ MHz$$

Next, we substitute into the modified Doppler equation:

$$v = \frac{(3 \times 10^8 \ m/sec.) \ (0.006 \ \cancel{MHz})}{2(7500 \ \cancel{MHz}) \cos 60}$$

$$v = 240 \ m/sec.$$

$$v = 240 \ \cancel{m/sec.} \times \frac{1 \ MPH}{0.447 \ \cancel{m/sec.}} = 537 \ MPH$$

Weather Prediction Using the Doppler Effect

The National Weather Service uses the Doppler Effect in the Nexrad (Next Generation Radar) weather prediction system. Microwaves are bounced off tiny droplets in the center of a cloud. The reflected waves are picked up by the radar system. In this way, it is possible to measure the velocity of wind currents within the clouds. The formation of a tornado can be predicted by using such measurements.

One location for a Nexrad system operated by the National Weather Service is at the Lewis University Airport in Romeoville, Illinois. This location services the entire greater Chicago area. Lewis University is the home school of the authors of this text.

Chapter XXV Problems

In all cases, the temperature is 68°F and the source is emitting a frequency of 440 Hz (A above middle C).

1. *What frequency is heard if the source is at rest and the observer moves away from the source with a speed of 60 MPH?*

2. *What frequency is heard if the source is at rest and the observer moves toward the source with a speed of 60 MPH?*

3. *What frequency is heard if the observer is at rest and the source moves toward him at 60 MPH?*

4. *What frequency is heard if the observer is at rest and the source moves away from him at 60 MPH?*

5. *A state patrolman on Interstate 55 sends out a radio wave signal of frequency 2×10^9 Hz to determine the speed of a fleeing car. The returning signal is less that the signal sent out. The frequency difference is 580 Hz. What is the speed of the fleeing car?*

6. *If a patrolman on Interstate 255 sends out a radio wave signal of frequency 1.5×10^9 Hz, and receives back a larger signal of frequency difference 380 Hz, what is the speed of the approaching car?*

7. *An aircraft uses Doppler equipment to measure ground speed. The angle of depression is 60° and the frequency of the radiation 7,800 MHz. The observed frequency shift is 8.2 kHz. What is the ground speed of the plane in MPH?*

8. *A plane is traveling at 600 MPH. The frequency of the radiation used in the Doppler equipment is 8,000 MHz and the angle of depression is 60°. What frequency shift (in kHz) will be observed?*

Answers to Problems

Chapter I

1. 7.22
2. 7.03
3. 7.65
4. 1.70
5. 8.83
6. 4.56×10^5
7. 4.57×10^{-4}
8. 2.37×10^4
9. 23,400
10. 0.000234
11. 490
12. 0.0000782
13. 35.6 ft.
14. 0.914 m
15. 511 m^3
16. 1140 ft.^{2}
17. 66.2 ft./sec.
18. 80.0 ft./sec.
19. 282 km/hr.
20. 226 MPH
21. 19,800 slugs

Chapter II

1. 4.59 kg
2. 225 N
3. 10.9 slugs
4. 755 lbs.
5. 1.5 lbs.
6. 1140 g
7. 564 lbs.
8. 17.1 gal.
9. 16,900 lbs.
10. 422 gal.
11. 0.8
12. 2.7
13. 0.922
14. 2.6

15. 49.5 lb./in.^{2}
16. 14.7 lb./in.^{2}
17. 52.5 lb./in.^{2}
18. 68°F
19. 5°F
20. 30°C
21. −20°C
22. 560°R
23. −10°F
24. 373°K
25. 110°C
26. 15°C
27. 752°F
28. 1,930°C

Chapter III

1. 0.45 m^3
2. 405 lb./in.^{2}
3. 76.7 lbs./in.^{2}
4. 7.05 ft.^{3}
5. 1.86 atmosphere
6. 3.26 m^3
7. −135°F
8. 50.1 lb./in.^{2}
9. 97.7 lb./in.^{2}
10. 25,100 ft.^{3}
11. 221 lb./in.^{2}
12. 0.387 ft.^{3}
13. 0.00750 slug/ft.^{3}
14. −4°C
15. 0.163 kg/m^3, 679 kg
16. 0.00188 slug/ft.^{3}
17. 24,400 ft.^{3}
18. 1.01 ft.^{3}
19. 0.00751 slug/ft.^{3}
20. 0.327 ft.^{3}
21. 0.161 ft.^{3}

Chapter IV

2. About 18,000 ft.

3. About 14,000 ft.

4. 67%   89%

5. 63%   5.2%

6. 96%   51%   Yes

Chapter V

1. 260 ft.

2. 131 ft.

3. -16.1 ft./sec.^{2}

4. 55 ft./sec.

5. -6.29 ft./sec.^{2}

6. 38.3 ft./sec.

7. 60 m

8. 244 ft.

9. 3.91 sec.

10. 100 ft.

11. 253 ft.

12. 165 ft.

13. 6.17 ft./sec.^{2}

14. 15.5 sec.

15. 203 ft./sec.

16. 140 ft./sec.^{2}

17. 16.7 ft./sec.^{2}

Chapter VI

1. 0.2 kg

2. 4 ft./sec.^{2}

3. 15 lb.

4. 24 lb.

5. 16 ft./sec.^{2}

6. 23,300 slugs; 746,000 lbs.

7. 25,400 N

8. 544 lb.

9. 5680 N

10. 257 kg

11. 132 ft./sec.

12. 16.8 slug

13. 976 lb.

14. 2150 ft./sec.

15. 1980 lb.

16. 16,400 N

17. 3640 N

18. 214,000 N

19. 47,500 N

Chapter VII

1. 3370 ft.-lb.

2. 15,000,000 J

3. 3180 ft.-lb.

4. -270 ft.-lb. (Note the negative sign!)

5. 5750 ft.-lb.

6. 1,700 lbs.

7. 140 lbs.   100 lbs.

8. 5180 ft.-lb.; 20,700 ft.-lb.

9. 39.2 J

10. 43.8 ft./sec.

11. 13.9 ft./sec.

12. 29.3 sec.

13. 0.182 HP

14. 8.18 HP   6.10 kW

15. 32.6 sec.

16. 8670 HP

17. 6930 HP

18. 477 MPH

19. 6190 lbs.

20.

	MODEL 0-235 C	MODEL 0-235 H	MODEL 0-235 L
indicated. HP (HP)	115	109	105 HP
P (PSI)	132 PSI	135	141
L (ft.)	0.323 ft.	0.323 ft.	0.323 ft.
A (in.^{2})	15.9 in.^{2}	15.9 in.	15.9 in.^{2}
N strokes/min.	1400	1300	1200
K	4	4	4

Chapter VIII

1. 2.81
2. 3.14
3. 74%
4. 83%
5. 15.8 ft.
6. 36.8 lbs.
7. 12.1 lbs.
8. 101 lbs.
9. 1,650 lbs.
10. 90.9%
11. 28.3 lbs.
12. 836 lbs.
13. 25.1 in.
14. 14.9 lbs.
15. 78.4%
16. 2.85 lbs.
17. 58.3 lbs.
18. 14.1°
19. 0.23 in.
20. 2.99 in.
21. 9.9°

Chapter IX

1. 480 rev./sec.   28,800 rev./min.
2. 22.5 rev.
3. 219 rev./min.
4. 24 sec.
5. 56.3 rev.
6. 89,000 ft.
7. 23.8 mi.
8. 2.34 rev./min.
9. 0.00199 rev./sec.^{2}

Chapter X

1. 26,200 lbs.
2. 53,100 lbs.
3. 89%
4. 8.81 ft.^{3}
5. 274 lbs.
6. 18,500 lbs.
7. 54.8 ft.^{3}

Chapter XI

1. 0.0632 ft.
2. 3.92 gal.
3. 29.4 gal.
4. 0.099 ft.
5. 250°F
6. 49 gal.
7. 1951 gal.
8. $110.25
9. 0.20 ft.
10. 34.6 gal.

Chapter XII

1. 1,710 Btu
2. 3,860 Btu
3. 60.5°F
4. 184°F
5. 110°F
6. 103°F
7. 82.4 lbs.
8. 128,000 Btu
9. 776,000 Btu
10. 485,000 Btu
11. 39.5°F
12. 27.8 lbs.
13. 2.51 lbs.
14. 8.74×10^6 Btu
15. 6.11 lbs.
16. 133 therms
17. 13,500 Btu/hr.
18. 12 lbs.; 13 lbs.
19. 4.74 lb.

Chapter XIII

1. 1,134 ft./sec.   771 MPH
2. 1,035 ft./sec.   704 MPH
3. 1,008 ft./sec.   686 MPH
4. 90 db
5. 50 db
6. 1.11
7. 1.25

Chapter XIV

1. 2870 ft.
2. 9.66 ft.
3. 13 mi.
4. 6.72 mi.   22.0 mi.
5. 8.69 m
6. 2860 km
7. 15.9 km
8. 7.7 mi.
9. 17.6 km
10. 1 hr. and 20 min. = 80 min.
11. 33.7°   12.3 cm
12. 51°
13. 81°

Chapter XV

1. **C:** 106 m, 52.5°
2. **E:** 13.9 mi., 178°
3. **H:** 52.5 m, 265°
4. **N:** 443 cm, 134°
5. **D:** 37.6 cm, 30 N of W or 60 W of N.
   The answer can also be expressed **D:** 37.6 cm, 150°
6. 188,000 lb., West
7. 37,000 lb., West
8. 453 N, 22° S of E

Chapter XVI

1. 193 MPH, 8.9° W of N
2. 181 MPH, 12.5° W of S
3. 190 MPH, 13.3° N of W
4. 174 MPH, 11.2° W of S
5. 232 MPH, 41.6° N of E
6. 236 MPH, 46.2° N of W
7. 155 MPH, N
8. 215 MPH, N
9. 140 MPH, 6.6° N of W
10. 223 MPH, 38.4 N of E
11. 186 MPH, 11.5° N of W

Chapter XVII

1. 40,000 lb.
2. 17,000 lb.
3. 458 ft.^{2}
4. 86.6 lb./ft.^{2} 0.367
5. 1,760 N/m^2 2.56
6. 1.79
7. 65,000 lb.
8. 253 MPH
9. 0.724   4520 ft.   196 knots
10. 0.373   5140 ft.   183 knots

Chapter XVIII

1. 3.56×10^{22} N
2. 17,000 MPH
3. 95 min.
4. 6,400 mi.
5. 1,550 mi.
6. 7700 m/sec.   1.5 hrs.

Chapter XIX

1. 3.24 m/sec.
2. 0.6 ft./sec.
3. 27.1 m/sec., East
4. 2.4 m/sec., East
5. 0.0999 m/sec.
6. 4.29 ft./sec., North
7. 67.7 MPH
8. The 3-kg ball is moving left at 1 m/sec. and the 2-kg ball is moving right at 4 m/sec.
9. The 2-kg ball is at rest and the 1-kg ball is moving east at 6 m/sec.
10. The 2-kg ball is moving right at 3 m/sec. and the 1-kg ball is moving right at 6 m/sec.

Chapter XX

1. T_1 =300 N and T_2 = 424 N
2. T = 695 lb. and C = 483 lb.
3. T = 1,250 lb. and C = 802 lb.
4. T = 1,960 lb. and T = 1,260 lb.
5. C = 549 N and T = 599 N
6. T = 805 lb. and C = 805 lb.
7. T_1 = 979 lb. and T = 725 lb.

Chapter XXI

1. T = 900 lbs.   H = 779 lbs.   V = 250 lbs.
2. T = 1170 lbs.   H = 755 lbs.   V = 404 lbs.

3. 36 kg-m^2

4. 12 kg-m^2

5. 0.75 rad./sec.^{2}

6. 2.67 rad./sec.

7. 3.43 rad./sec.

8. 0.188 slug/ft.^{2}

Chapter XXII

1. 0.0139 in.

2. 0.0310 in.^{3}

3. 172 lbs.

4. 16,500 lbs.

5. 4,750 lbs.

6. 0.00862 in.

7. 1.67 in.^{2} 1.84 in.^{2}

8. 0.00993 in.

9. 0.0583 ft.^{3}

10. 0.00313 ft.^{3}

11. 0.45 in.^{2} 0.75 in.^{2}

Chapter XXIII

1. $y = 1.5 \sin \left(\dfrac{360\,x}{1.1} + 25° \right)$

2. 0.61 ft.

3. 4.44 Hz

4. 3 ft./sec.

5. 1.15 ft.

6. $y = 0.2 \sin \left(\dfrac{360\,x}{0.8} \right)$

7. −0.141 ft. The leaf is below the water level.

Chapter XXIV

1. 3.16 m

2. 7.5×10^{17} Hz

3. 600 kilohertz

4. 2×10^8 m/sec.

5. 1.46

6. 1.24×10^8 m/sec.

Chapter XXV

1. 407 Hz

2. 474 Hz

3. 477 Hz

4. 408 Hz

5. 97 MPH

6. 85 MPH

7. 705 MPH

8. 7.15 kHz

TABLE OF CONVERSION FACTORS

LENGTH

1 in. = 2.54 cm

1 m = 9.37 in. = 3.281 ft.

1 ft. = 0.3048 m

12 in. = 1 ft.

3 ft. = 1 yd.

1 yd. = 0.9144 m

1 km = 0.621 mi.

1 mi. = 1.609 km = 5,280 ft.

AREA

$1 \text{ m}^2 = 0.76 \text{ ft.}^2$

$1 \text{ m}^2 = 10,000 \text{ cm}^2$

$1 \text{ ft.}^2 = 0.0929 \text{ m}^2 = 144 \text{ in.}^2$

$1 \text{ in.}^2 = 6.452 \text{ cm}^2$

VOLUME

$1 \text{ m}^3 = 1,000,000 \text{ cm}^3$

$1 \text{ ft.}^3 = 1728 \text{ in.}^3 = 0.0283 \text{ m}^3$

$1 \text{ liter} = 1000 \text{ cm}^3 = 1.0576 \text{ qt.}$

$1 \text{ ft.}^3 = 7.481 \text{ gal.}$

$1 \text{ gal.} = 3.786 \text{ liters} = 231 \text{ in.}^3$

MASS

$1 \text{ amu} = 1.66 \times 10^{-27} \text{kg}$

1000 kg = 1 metric ton

1000 g = 1 kg

1 slug = 14.59 kg

FORCE AND WEIGHT

1 N = 0.2248 lb.

1 lb. = 4.448 N

1 lb. = 16 oz.

VELOCITY

1 MPH = 1.47 ft./sec.

1 m/sec. = 3.281 ft./sec.

60 MPH = 88 ft./sec.

1 knot = 1.688 ft./sec.

1 knot = 1.151 MPH

1 knot = 1.852 km/hr.

1 MPH = 1.61 km/hr.

PRESSURE

1 atm = 76.0 cmHg

$1 \text{ atm} = 14.7 \text{ lb./in.}^2$

$1 \text{ Pa} = 0.000145 \text{ lb./in.}^2$

$1 \text{ bar} = 14.5 \text{ lb./in.}^2$

TIME

1 year = 365 days

1 day = 24 hr. = 1,440 min.

ENERGY

1 J = 0.738 ft. lb.

1 cal = 4.186 J

1 Btu = 252 cal.

POWER

1 HP = 550 ft. lb./sec.

1 HP = 0.746 kW

1 W = 1 J/sec.

1 W = 0.738 ft. lb./sec.

1 Btu/hr. = 0.293 W

FUNDAMENTAL CONSTANT

g = 32 lb./slug

= 9.8 N/kg